Dancing into Darkness

Dancing into Darkness

Based on a true story

Deborah Wardle

TRICORN
BOOKS

www.tricornbooks.co.uk

Dancing into Darkness
Deborah Wardle

ISBN 978 0 9573435 3 5
A CIP catalogue record for this book is available from the British Library.

Published 2012 by Tricorn Books,
a trading name of 131 Design Ltd.
131 High Street, Old Portsmouth,
PO1 2HW

www.tricornbooks.co.uk

Printed & bound by Berforts Group Ltd

Unreserved thanks go to my solicitor, whose trust and faith over three years never once wavered. She gave her all to my case, even when the powers-that-be refused her fee, she gave her time freely.

'Thank you, Rebecca.'

My daughters, who suffered pain, fear and violence, but who never asked for explanations. They have given me their unfaltering love, trust and support throughout the years, without which this book might never have been written.

'Anna and Lilly - I love you very much.'

Contents

Introduction

Introduction

Hi, my names Jeannette.

At the age of twenty-three, I found myself caught up in something - completely out of my control. I could do nothing but watch as my life spiralled into insignificance.

My dream as a young child was like any other little girls; to marry the man of my dreams and have a happy family life. Unfortunately, life took those dreams and quashed them. My path took a totally unforeseen direction.

My tragic but inspirational story shows the inner strength no-one realises they have until a harrowing situation brings it to the surface. It hasn't been an easy story to tell and it has taken years to be brave enough to face the truth. Reliving the emotions of guilt, fear and self-hatred buried deep within - was a painful experience. Why have I decided to tell such a story of cruelty? Because my story isn't special; it's one of many unheard, ignored and brushed under the carpet, which cause irreparable damage that can silently last a lifetime. It was my trusting, loving and forgiving nature which led me into the traumatic experience which eventually left me facing a prison sentence. Though my stubborn and strong-willed attitude helped my survival; others may not be as lucky.

This is not a story of forgiveness or of revenge.

It is a story of truth; I know because it happened - to me.

An Unexpected Escape

The gate slammed shut behind me. I heard the clattering of metal as the latch grabbed the catch. It sent a shudder down my spine as it had done on numerous occasions before - causing my body to tremble uncontrollably with fearful expectation.

I gripped the pushchair firmly in both hands, quickened my pace and fled for my life.

My throat began to swell with the bruising caused by his attempt to strangle me and I was finding it hard to breathe. The gasps for air burnt my chest as my hastily striding legs struggled to carry my skeletal frame. My hands kept a tight hold on the rickety carriage securing my twenty-month-old baby. Too scared to look behind me, I gathered speed as I charged down the familiar steep hill. My feet hurt as they felt the uneven pavement beneath me. Every cracked slab or loosened stone pierced through the thinning, worn-out soles of my grubby trainers. A small plastic grocery bag containing the handful of Lilly's belongings I had escaped with - swung like a balloon flying in the wind around her as she laughed with excitement at the bumpy joyride she was experiencing.

'Faster mummy,' she yelled, enjoying the thrill of the ride.

My heart thumped - each beat echoed inside my head. The intensity of burning filled my tightening chest as I gathered momentum down the hill. The sun was still high, its rays burning into my shoulders and adhering to the glistening droplets of perspiration forming through my exertion. I could feel my face swelling as I puffed and panted in an attempt to control the straining of my lungs. Breathing became difficult. I longed to stop and catch my breath but I had to continue. Feeling light-headed I struggled to stay conscious, my eyes were filling with

1

the beads of sweat dripping from my brow. The feeling of panic set in as I realised what I had done, but I had no time for it to take control. I couldn't stop, I dare not. As I neared the road at the bottom of the hill I scanned for passing cars, thankfully the roads were empty. I quickly but carefully manoeuvred the pushchair across the curb-stones, trying not to tip it over in my terrorised state. Feeling faint, I felt exhaustion taking hold. I thought the shaking of my hands were due to the pushchair's vibration until I had slowly crossed to the opposite pavement: it was then I realised it was emanating from deep within. Fear had taken over and fighting it was an obstacle I could do without. I used the adrenalin to encourage my legs to run faster. Drawing level with the pub on the opposite side of the road, a place I had visited on many occasions, I hoped no-one would come out at that particular moment. Being a local girl, everyone knew me. I hadn't time for explanations or 'hellos' - after all, none of them would protect me or Lilly; I knew I was alone in my quest for freedom. A few steps more and I was level with my grandparents' vacated house. I remembered the happy times at their house as a young child, but knew this was no time for memories. I reached the telephone box where I used to ring my parents to say I had arrived safely at my grandparents' on a Sunday afternoon. For a fleeting moment I thought - maybe I had time before he caught up with me to ring dad, in the hope he would save me from this monster. I decided not to stop. I had to keep running, faster than I had ever run before; my life depended on it. I ran past my aunt and uncle's house, looking into their window as I fled past like a whirlwind. I couldn't go taking trouble to their door anyway it was too close to 202, and I had to get to safety. Facing me was a hill as steep as the one I had just descended. I was feeling hot and sweating profusely; my legs began to buckle beneath me.

'No, no please don't, not far now, come on, you can do it. You must,' I demanded of myself as tears tried to force their way through my eyes.

I prayed to God to give me the strength to keep going. I seemed to have been running for a lifetime; each minute felt an hour long. Still, I daren't stop to catch a breath. I started to cough and splutter as I felt my throat closing up. My stomach began to churn, but having not eaten that day I knew I wouldn't vomit. My head felt like it was about to explode with the intensity of emotion that was building. With one final deep breath held inside and with all the strength I could muster, I pushed Lilly to the top of the hill. Reaching level ground my legs begged for a rest; pain was ripping through them. I needed to switch off from the aching muscles in case I got cramp. I had become an expert in switching off from pain; it was the only way to survive. My chest began to ease and the burning subsided as my breathing calmed. As I dared to slow down I heard.

'Faster - mummy - faster,' followed by her little giggle.

Lilly's giggle usually commanded all my attention as I enjoyed the rare laughter of my baby. My only comfort was thinking she knew nothing of what was happening, even though just a few minutes earlier - she had saved my life.

I reached the small chapel at the end of the road. It was the spot where, at the age of five, I fell out of dad's moving car. That injury seemed bad at the time but was insignificant compared with the injuries I had received over the last two years. I couldn't sense Billy close nor could I hear his footsteps in pursuit. I prayed again he wouldn't be there as I steeled myself for a quick glance behind me. The unexpected movement caused a jolt that ripped through the soreness of my swelling throat. My eyes dared to scan the pavement behind me; to my relief he wasn't there, so I allowed myself to stop for a minute to rest. Looking around, my eyes searched for anyone who might recognise me and alert Billy to my whereabouts. Luckily the street was empty so I allowed myself a breather, still gripping the pushchair in my terror until some energy returned. I knew an attempt to make it to my parents' house was out of the question there was a chance Billy had cut across the fields leading down to the corner of their street. I was aware he could be waiting for me. Passing the cemetery and entering the park would leave me vulnerable. I knew he wouldn't let me permanently get away. I worried this was one of his sadistic games, letting me think I'd escaped, only to drag me back to the house of horror which allowed him to put me through hours of torture and pain. I couldn't afford for him to catch us, not now I had got this far. I made a quick decision

3

to go to the nearest place of safety. Knowing we were both in serious danger I found myself being drawn towards the home that had witnessed many of his assaults. At least his parents' house could give me temporary shelter and if I was very lucky Dave, his brother, might be home. He was the only one who had the bravery to stand up to Billy. Their house was only a few yards away. All my hopes were pinned on Dave as I cornered the road; in my heart I was hoping Dave would protect me.

I flung open their door with gusto and barged into the in-laws' house. I lifted Lilly, still seated in her pushchair, into the kitchen. I fell through the door - having tripped through panic - over the two large concrete steps leading into the house. Billy's shocked mother jumped out of her seat at my unexpected, undignified entrance. I was more concerned with getting Lilly safely indoors than with anyone's reaction.

'He's going to kill me, help me, please, help me,' I screamed.

Lilly's innocent smile turned to her usual crying as she sensed fear in my voice. I lifted her out of her carriage and hugged her tightly to my chest in an effort to comfort her, but also in an attempt to prevent Billy's mother taking her from me.

'What the hell's going on? Don't come up here with your troubles.'

Billy's mother rushed towards me trying to shut the door, pushing me outside. I stood rigid.

'If he gets hold of me he will kill me,' I repeated hoping for her help. 'Where's Dave?'

My throat was now very sore and had almost closed up, making my voice forced as I strained to be heard.

'He's not here, why?' his mother snapped in response. 'He won't help you.'

I could hear her voice begin to tremble as she realised something serious was occurring. I felt my heart sink knowing Billy could turn up at any moment and his mother would happily shove Lilly and me out - rather than cope with his wrath. During my pleas for help, his father sat unperturbed in his armchair, his eyes never leaving the horse racing; he seemed a cold, unfeeling man.

'What the hell's gone off?' Billy's mother cried nervously,

believing her son was in pursuit and would soon arrive. She was afraid of him as much as me, but while he had me for a victim he gave his family peace.

'You can't stay here. I don't want his violence up here,' she said running to look out of the door, expecting his imminent arrival.

'Please,' I begged 'please can you go to the phone box and ring my dad?'

'Why can't you go?' she retorted, her head still hanging out of the door.

'I'm frightened; if he catches me he will kill me. If he finds me here it won't be so bad. Please Vera, seriously, I need help.'

She turned towards me, her eyes furious, her lips pouting in anger, emphasising the wrinkled skin around her mouth. I couldn't take 'no' for an answer. I shoved dad's phone number in her hand. Her expression changed as she felt my trembling hand touch hers. I saw the glimmer of sympathy appear in her eyes, for a split second I saw sorrow appear amidst the hardness of her scowl. Quickly she turned her head away from me. Chuntering to herself, she grabbed her purse and shot out of the door and down the path. In her absence I folded Lilly's pushchair, enabling me to run to dad's car as soon as it arrived; for all the times I had let him down in the past I knew he would come to my aid. I cuddled Lilly in my arms, calming her confused state. I wasn't sure in my panicked mind whether Vera would ring my father or Billy. I had no trust in her; after all I had Lilly with me, which meant I was taking her granddaughter away from her family. I felt sick with anticipation as I stood helpless, knowing I had to rely on her. I turned to look at his father - still motionless in his chair. I knew he could sense me watching him but still he ignored me, not even making the effort to speak to his granddaughter. I knew Vera had led a similar life for most of their married life and maybe that's why Vera eventually gave in to my pleas. I picked up the carrier bag containing Lilly's few belongings; holding Lilly in my left arm and the bag in my hand, I picked up the folded pushchair with my right when I heard footsteps nearing the gate. The gate opened: for a split second I couldn't move. Riveted by fear, my first thought was the sight of Billy. I knew he would drag me out of the house and my fate would be sealed. His parents knew his temper and violence but not to the degree I had endured it. As I listened to the footsteps nearing the door, each step caused a sickness to my core; tears of relief welled in my eyes at Vera's appearance.

'Come on quickly,' she said quietly, 'your dad's on his way.'

'Thank you, thank you,' I sobbed amid the flow of uncontrollable tears.

I stepped out onto the top step where Vera made a grab for her granddaughter, instinctively I lifted the pushchair in front of us - she was forced to take that instead. Her look was cold, all empathy had disappeared as she realised what she had done and that she would get the brunt of Billy's anger. Still, I doubted she had rung my father. I knew how afraid of her son she was and there was a possibility she would put him first. She turned to head down the paved path. I seemed to be forcing my feet to move as pangs of dread surged through my body.

'Come on,' she repeated, her voice more agitated and panicked.

Cautiously, with my heart pounding and my stomach churning, I made my way down the next step clutching onto my little girl. As my feet touched the path I could feel my body trembling. I somehow held myself up as my buckling legs continued to fight me. My teeth began to chatter as fear intensified. Slowly making my way down towards the gate behind the old woman I looked to my left, knowing this would be the direction in which Billy would appear. I swallowed hard, though my mouth was dry through nerves. Billy's absence was a blessing. I heard the sound of dad's car pull up outside the small gate; relieved, my tears began to fall but I quickly managed to control my emotions, crying wouldn't solve anything at this precise moment. I had to be strong for Lilly who was by now very afraid, sensing her mummy's state of mind. I focused on getting to dad's car and locking us in before my executioner arrived. I knew dad being there wouldn't deter Billy's violence. He would take Lilly from me no matter what, and I knew I couldn't leave her with him under any circumstances. As I reached the gate Vera turned to speak. She saw the terror in my eyes and in our silent stare we seemed to understand each other.

'You'll be alright with your dad,' her voice sounded softer, a more sorrowful tone.

A forced smile appeared on her saddened face. I knew she was frightened; both of us knew she would be the first in line for Billy's temper, especially if his father gladly told him she had helped me take his daughter from him. I couldn't think about anyone else except Lilly and me; our safety was paramount. Vera reached to take Lilly out of my arms; just then I felt I could trust her. She hugged her granddaughter and kissed her goodbye, not knowing if she would ever see her again. She handed her back, with tears falling slowly down her worn, wrinkled cheeks. I refused to feel sorry for her; selfish maybe, but now it was self-preservation. I took my daughter from her and without looking back I cautiously walked towards dad's waiting car. He climbed out of the driver's seat and headed towards the rear of the car. Opening the boot, he asked,

'Is that all you have?' His face looking puzzled.

'It's all I need. I have Lilly.'

My heart continued to thump as I let myself believe I was almost away. I needed dad to be quick but I knew he wouldn't see the urgency of the situation. I climbed into the car, thankful to be shutting the door and gripping my arms tightly around my little girl. Lilly wriggled to get free of my hold. I heard the driver's door slam. I stared toward the end of the road in fear of Billy's appearance. The car ignition started and slowly the car pulled away. Dad's voice became a blur as he asked me questions, I continually scanned the road ahead; the trepidation of seeing Billy heading towards his mother's house engulfed all my senses. I lowered my head, burying my face in the softness of Lilly's hair. I took a deep breath, inhaling the sweet smell of my daughter. In my mind's eye - I saw Anna. The pain of her pretty face seemed unbearable to endure. I opened my eyes – looking straight ahead as dad drove down the road and away from any immediate danger. I stayed silent, even though Lilly showed excitement at being in the car with her grandad. The journey was short - just a matter of minutes. As we rounded the corner towards my childhood home, subconsciously I searched for Billy thankfully he was nowhere to be seen.

'Well, now you're away from him, I hope you don't intend going back.'

'Never', I answered, determined but solemn as the enormity of my actions sank in.

'Well, my girl, you have two daughters by two different dads. How many more are you going to have?' I sensed annoyance in his voice.

'Dad,' I said, in a tone to say 'I don't need this now'. 'I could have a dozen kids by a dozen different dads and I will love them all the same.'

'I know you would,' he replied, his tone softer as he realised this wasn't a time for recriminations. He didn't pass any further comments.

The car pulled to a halt and dad alighted without speaking. I heard him open the boot and take out the pushchair and the bag containing all I had escaped with. He neared the passenger door but realised I hadn't unlocked it. I felt his eyes on me as I held Lilly close to my breast; he sensed I needed a few minutes to myself and decided to leave me to my thoughts and contemplation. Lilly had fallen asleep, clutched in my tight grip. I could hear her innocent sighs, which caused my tears to appear. Until an hour ago tears had no place in my life. Billy's bullying had become a way of life; he had taken control until I was void of emotion. I no longer knew who I was; I had become numb to emotion. In those few minutes alone in the car while Lilly slept, the realisation of the extent of what he had done began to dawn on me. I was away from Billy but far from feeling happy, I felt strange; everything felt surreal. I wasn't even sure this was actually happening. Maybe it was another dream. I had begged God so many times after a beating or attack to end the torture my children and I were experiencing that maybe this was like all the other times - I would awake to see the monster that terrorised us - facing me waiting, with that grin on his face.

I couldn't trust anyone - why should I? No-one had helped me, not till today. I didn't know what love meant anymore; he had beaten everything but fear out of me. Billy's continual barrage of insults, belittling and victimisation made me feel unworthy of love and after Anna's ordeal - I felt I didn't deserve to be loved. I took a deep breath, filling my lungs with the scent of Lilly. I knew I had to protect her, whatever the consequences.

6.15pm September 20th

My thoughts were interrupted as Lilly sighed and moaned, wriggling around for a more comfortable position. I realised that, in my need to hold her close, I was gripping her too tight. I could see clearly across the park. I reflected on the many years I had played alone with my doll (my grandad had bought me), on the swings before I was old enough to attend school. Soon the years of fun and games with all the kids of the area filled my mind, coaxing a smile of happier times. My eyes wandered to the gate in the top left-hand corner; this was the way Billy would come in his search for me when he realised I had made it to my parents. Scanning the park for reassurance, I allowed my eyes to drift up the road; thinking nothing allowed my mind a few minutes of calm. I rested my left cheek on the top of Lilly's head. I felt the warmth of her tiny fragile body snuggling into my ribs. I listened to her soft gentle breathing which seemed to comfort me. My gaze fixed on a figure in the distance; I recognised the tall fair-headed man walking towards me: it was Adam - the friend I had shared my childhood with. As he grew larger and nearer to where dad's car was parked. I was afraid he would recognise me; in my shame I averted my eyes and buried my head into Lilly's soft blonde hair - silently begging him to pass by. To my relief he did.

For over two years I had been subservient to a monster, Lilly's father. All that was good about him I held in my arms and she was beautiful. The feeling of actually escaping him dawned on me: I knew then I would never be safe.

Lilly took a deep breath as I felt her waking up. I watched her stretch her little limbs. I took one more safety glance over the park and the road around me and nervously began to unlock the car door.

'Hello sweetheart,' I gently said, placing her in my right arm. Cautiously still scanning around me, I opened the door. Putting one foot on the pavement I felt excruciating pain. I tried to lift myself out of the seat. Dad immediately appeared to aid me. He must have been watching out of the kitchen window to ensure our safety; his help was appreciated in my struggle to walk. Taking Lilly in his arms and offering me his hand in support, he said,

'Come on in, you're safe now'.

I smiled as I took his hand, but his words meant nothing. I would never be safe, but at least for now the beatings had stopped. I wondered what welcome would await me from my mother. I hadn't seen or spoken to her since the attack on Anna. I felt sick to my stomach as I walked into the house that, only a few weeks before, I had promised never to return to.

'Don't worry,' dad said in a comforting voice as he placed Lilly on the floor of the kitchen. I half smiled as I remembered mum doing the same to me all those years ago when, at a similar age, we first moved into this house. I picked Lily up, not wanting her to be away from me. Making my way into the living room I saw the fire wasn't lit - the house seemed cold and daunting, far from the warmth I remembered in the days of my youth. Sitting on the settee, I steeled myself for mum's appearance. Dad entered the room with some of Anna's old toys from where they were housed in the cubbyhole under the stairs.

'Your mum will be in soon. She is with some people up at the kennels but she knows you're here,' he said as he placed the toys on the floor in front of Lilly. 'Jeannette, stop worrying, your mum isn't angry with you anymore.'

He disappeared into the kitchen and put the kettle on to make a pot of tea. When the telephone rang, he shut the connecting door as he went to answer it. I sat quietly watching Lilly playing with her new exciting toys. Sadly my mind wandered to my lost little girl, my Anna. I placed my head on the back of the settee in an attempt to relax and stop my quivering body as I fought back the tears that were needing to break free of my control.

7.20pm September 20th

The sound of Lilly's laughter encouraged my eyes to open. I saw dad enjoying his time with her and the toys.

'Look, mummy has woken up, Lilly' he said as he sat cross-legged on the floor surrounded by dolls.

I remember how much he loved Anna at this age and took her everywhere with him. Lilly had missed out on her grandparents over her twenty months due to the conditions we had been living under. She had missed out on the interaction with my family, only having the odd hour with my parents. To see her fussing around dad like this gave me a sense of pleasure, if only for a few minutes.

'Your tea's gone cold but thought it better to leave you to sleep,' said dad caringly.

I hadn't been sleeping. I had been somewhere else in my mind trying to piece together how I ended up here, a physical and mental wreck. I hurt so much, not only physically but mentally. I felt so very sad and alone. I hurt and ached from the top of my head to the tip of my toes. Sitting in peaceful surroundings I felt for the first time how much my body was crying out for peace. I was badly injured, the bruises always reminded me of that - but the fact I wasn't being harassed, bullied or beaten made me realise how normal Billy's behaviour towards me had become. I heard mum making her way down the path towards the gate. I listened to her voice as she said farewell to the visitors she had been dealing with, preventing our meeting an hour or so earlier. Her voice was soft and gentle; so different to the voice I heard on our last meeting, full of rage and disgust. She knew I had arrived, but Friday was her busy day at the kennels. Anyway, I wasn't in any rush for her lecture or 'I told you so'. I had never seen her as angry as the last day I was here. I couldn't blame her and I understood why she acted the way she did. Unfortunately her anger only fuelled Billy's control over me and the truth I had come to tell her; and the plea for help never materialised. I knew the separation from my parents would please Billy, leaving his plan for my demise to go uninterrupted. I wasn't afraid of mum, just her words; after all, the truth hurts. The door opened and in she came. Through nerves, I immediately stood in preparation for the theatrics of blame. Dad got up from the floor and picked Lilly up, taking her discreetly out of the way.

'Let's go and see the doggies,' he told her, heading out of the door.

This only served to make my apprehension worse as she headed towards me.

'Thank God you're safe,' she cried with tears filling her eyes.

Her arms were stretched out, reaching towards me, open and inviting. Shocked and relieved, I sank into them sobbing uncontrollably. I hadn't felt love for a very long time and being back in mum's arms I realised - I wasn't hated as Billy had drilled into me. She began to cry, her hold getting tighter. The flow of tears between us wouldn't stop. I sobbed so hard I felt my heart breaking, with all the pent-up hidden emotions inside of me.

'The bastard!' It was unheard-of that mum would swear.

I knew she had felt my bones as she hugged me and had realised the extent of fear and control I had been living under.

'I didn't beat Anna, mum. I came down to tell you the truth and ask for help. I can't live without her - but I had to let her go - and to let you all believe it was me - for Lilly's sake. He threatened to kill her and he wouldn't let me out of the house with her and he said he would kill me if I left him, and all of you.' My sobbing escalated the more I tried to speak. 'I didn't care if he killed me, but you and dad … he scares me mum, I'm so scared'

'Shush.' She stopped me from continuing in my fraught state.

'My God, what has he done to you? I promise he will never hurt you again,' she loosened her hold of me. 'Come on try to calm down, you're safe now, sit down I'll make you a drink.'

I knew she wouldn't be able to keep her promise but her intentions were good and it was what I needed to hear at the time. Billy was too violent and he hadn't any conscience. His hatred for all women put every female in danger, even little girls. Sitting alone, my stomach still contracting from the sobs, I started to worry I had brought trouble into my parents' lives, something I had been trying to prevent. On top of the fear I began to feel guilt. Mum walked in with a tray containing the mugs of tea and a plate of biscuits. I felt her eyes burning into me as she tried to come to terms with her daughter, once a vibrant, bubbly girl who was so full of life, being a worn-out, tormented, terrified wreck.

'Here, drink this, you look starved.' Silence fell between us, both lost for words. 'You're safe now,' she repeated. I think both my parents needed to believe I was at last safe. 'I'm sorry for ever thinking you had anything to do with what happened to Anna. Mark came down after Anna had told him the truth. I felt so guilty but had no way of getting in touch with you to apologise. I didn't want to come up and make things more difficult for you and Lilly. I'm sorry.'

I couldn't answer her. Mum wasn't one to apologise for anything because normally she was spot on with her intuition. She had no need to apologise; her warm arms were all I needed. She told me Anna had been a regular visitor to them since she had gone to live with her daddy. Mum tenderly explained,

'Anna is doing fine now. She's moved schools and seems happy. Mark's been very good with her and about time too,' adding a little sarcastic laugh, trying to lighten the situation.

I hadn't seen my eight-year-old daughter since I made her leave - except for odd painful occasions we met on the street. But the circumstances made it impossible for the exchange of words between us, let alone a cuddle or a kiss. Except that is, for one occasion a few weeks ago. I missed her so much but felt I didn't deserve to be her mummy.

Mum continued as I sat, too emotional to join in the conversation.

'She has recovered well, though I know she doesn't blame you for anything.'

'She should,' I remarked feeling ashamed.

'She misses you so much, Jeannette. And little Lilly; we all have. She always talks about you when she is here; she really understands more than you give her credit for. She obviously went through hell but she won't say anything against you. You're her mummy and she needs you as much now as she ever did.' Mum's smile gave me reassurance that she believed the truth now. 'Mark and his family came down to discuss things with us and we all agreed not to take her assault any further because if you were taking the blame, it was because you were in danger. We had no way of knowing how much and coming in heavy-handed, or involving the authorities, could have been worse for Lilly and you.'

I lifted my eyes from staring at my cup; it seemed to be sinking in that they really did know the truth and, though I still blamed myself, they did not.

'No matter what happened between you and Mark he was adamant from the start you couldn't have done that to Anna. He knows you better than you think, even better than me it seems,' she continued as she bowed her head as if ashamed. 'I'm sorry I didn't listen to you that day you were here. I was so angry when I saw her bruised and battered little body. Your dad deep down knew you hadn't got it in you to hurt anyone like that, least of all your own child.'

I could see her sadness for doubting me; I moved towards her and hugged her. I told her everything was my fault, and it was. The tears began to stream down my face. She felt them as our faces touched, as we parted, she saw the bruises around my neck.

'Oh my God.'

'It's okay mum, I'm alive, that's what counts, but I'm frightened he will come down here after he's been drinking tonight. He will know where I am when he doesn't find me at his mam's house.'

'Don't you worry about him I won't let him hurt you anymore, you're home now, you're safe, and in time you may even have your Anna back, but we must take one day at a time. You go and have a bath - it will calm you; give Lilly one too. You can sleep in my room. I will use the boys' old room - dad sleeps in your old room now. Come on, take your things up.'

'I haven't any things, mum, not even a nightie,' explaining how I had duped him with the bags.

'Quick thinking,' she said. 'Go run the bath. I will find you a few things till morning and you can go with your dad to pick your belongings up.'

I didn't relish that idea, but I knew it had to be done.

I fetched Lilly from the kennel area where she was fussing one of the older show dogs.

'Is everything alright?' Dad asked as he placed Lilly into my arms.

I nodded. I knew if I tried to speak I would start crying again. I wasn't used to anyone being nice to me.

'Come on little lady,' I whispered, holding back all the emotion that was welling up inside. 'Bath time for you.'

I knew I wouldn't get any arguments from Lilly. She loved

her baths and I loved to bathe her: it was one of the few times I knew I could spend uninterrupted time with her. Billy hated bathing her. Billy hated everything.

Mum followed me upstairs and disappeared into her room. I continued to the bathroom to run a warm bubble bath for Lilly, who was excited at the thought of a bath at mamma's house. As I placed her amongst the bubbles and put a sponge into her hands, she smiled at me. She flicked the bubbles at me as I sat close to the side of the bath, and it made us both giggle. She could always sense my unhappiness and did all she could to make me laugh. She was a bright child.

'Much too big for you but at least they will do tonight while I wash yours.' Mum handed me a pair of joggers and a T-shirt while peeping around the bathroom door, 'I have left you a nightie on the bed.'

I thanked her, and she left me alone with my baby. A sense of calm came over me. I looked at Lilly playing gleefully amongst the bubbles without a worry in the world. She counted on me to keep her safe, but then so had Anna. The guilt I felt over Anna engulfed me. I fought back the tears as I got down on the floor at the side of the bath to play in the bubbles with Lilly. It was the first time my mind dared to think about my missing child. I wondered if she would ever forgive me. If I had to wait until she grew up I knew it would be worth it. All I wanted now was my daughters to be close, but for now Lilly needed the protection to prevent what happened to Anna - happening to her.

We returned downstairs, Lilly in her nightdress and with a gleaming smile.

'Come and eat your supper, little lady,' dad shouted from the kitchen as we walked through the passage door.

She ran into the kitchen and climbed up on a chair, but seeing what was on the table didn't impress her at all. Looking at her, dad laughed saying,

'Doesn't she like salad?'

I smiled 'Supper to Lilly is cereals: do you have any?'

'We do,' laughing he turned to the cupboard, 'Weetabix or Cornflakes?'

Lilly pointed to the Weetabix box.

'When you take Lilly to bed, you have a soak in the bath and have a little time to yourself,' mum said, 'no-one will disturb you.' Her smile was comforting.

'Thank you mum, I will,' I replied as I sat trying to eat a little salad.

I didn't eat much: my throat had virtually closed and felt very sore, so swallowing was virtually impossible. After Lilly had eaten she said goodnight to her grandparents and we disappeared upstairs. As I put her to bed she asked where her daddy was. I told her to go to sleep and held her hand as she snuggled down into her mamma's bed. Within minutes she was sleeping and content. I kissed her lightly on her forehead and quietly left the room, closing the door behind me. I headed towards the bathroom and turned on the taps. I sat watching the bath fill while the bubbles cascaded under the running water. I wasn't used to time alone. Quiet time was non-existent in my turmoil of a life. Once I was in the hot steamy water, I slid down until my painfully bruised body had totally been covered. I didn't want to see the colourful marks and scars of torment and torture. All was quiet and peaceful; it felt very strange. I lay listening for the commotion of Billy's arrival - I couldn't believe he hadn't yet appeared. Maybe my dad was right; maybe he wouldn't come here. Although I had learnt not to take anything for granted, there was at least hope. I gently cleansed myself, avoiding the most painful areas. The sweet perfume of the bubble bath disguised my usual smell of fear. I closed my eyes and relaxing in the hot soapy water, I remembered.

Meeting Billy

November 20th 1982.

The music was pumping as my friends and I reached the door of the in-place to be at the time. The two burly bouncers held the large glass doors open as soon as we arrived. We were full of high spirits, each sporting a beaming smile as the beat of the Boy George hit 'Do You Really Want to Hurt Me' blasted out in the lounge area.

'Evening, girls,' flirted the handsome doormen sporting black suits, white frilled shirts and red bow ties. Heading through the door towards the draw of the music, I was filled with excitement. I had spent so long on my own after the split from my husband. I felt I had missed out on the nightlife a young girl should enjoy. Being married at seventeen after falling pregnant stemmed any ideas of dancing and partying. I began to feel like I had restarted my life and was looking forward to a bright and lively future. Bumping into old school chums and past childhood sweethearts added to the thrill of being me. We fought our way through the dancers to get to the three-people-deep bar. I had the knack of wiggling my way through to the bar and getting served quite quickly; it was usually my smile that did it. I ordered our drinks and waited. I found my eyes searching around the bar area in the hope of seeing any further friends or family; my brothers and cousins frequented the same bars, so it was always nice to see them and say, 'Hi' or sometimes have a more in-depth conversation if we hadn't seen each other for a while. As I scanned the room I saw a piercing pair of ice-blue eyes staring back at me; they belonged to a tall man with dark spikey hair, who was sporting a Clint Eastwood beard, and I loved beards. He smiled and I coyly smiled back then continued my scan for family and friends. The barman arrived with our drinks. I handed the money over while passing the drinks behind me to my four companions. On receiving the change, I picked up my drink and followed my friends to a table where we remained for the rest of the evening. We danced to the tunes we liked and had a few more drinks. I noticed a few times the man's gaze was following me around the room. My friend had also noticed and commented on the fact I had an admirer. I wasn't a regular visitor to this particular pub, or to any pub for that matter, so I put it down to the fact I was a new face. I had never seen him before but everyone else seemed know him; he was always in conversation with someone when I casually glanced his way. I noticed he was with another man who seemed to be watching me too and it was him that asked me to dance when the music slowed down at the end of the evening. I thanked him but graciously refused. Suddenly I felt someone very close behind me. I was spun around by my hand and was led to the dance floor. For some reason I didn't argue, I followed his lead. We danced to 'All the Love in the World' sung by Dionne Warwick: It felt very romantic. He smelt nice and his arms seemed to enclose me as I melted into them. By the time the next song played I was in a world of warmth and pleasure, something I had missed for a while.

'What's your name? I've asked around but no-one would tell me.'

I smiled 'Jeannette. They call me Jeannie.'

'Where are you from?' His interest continued.

'Here.'

He seemed surprised I was a local girl.

'I'm Billy. Billy Burnshaw,' his expression inquiring if I knew or had heard of him – I hadn't, 'can I walk you home?'

'I'm with my friends, but thank you anyway.' I declined nicely but as I looked for my friends they were nowhere to be found.

'Looks like they have left you,' he smiled, 'come on - you're safe with me.'

Before I knew it his arm was around me and I was being led through the remainder of the smooching couples on the dance floor; soon we had exited into the night's air. His friend appeared and asked if we wanted a lift. I was a little unsure but saw he had a girl with him. I thought 'it's only down the road I'm sure I'll be safe', so I thanked him and got into his car. Billy introduced his friend as Pete and the girl as Sue. Sue and I chatted as Pete drove; she seemed a little loud and rough in her speech with every other word being a swear word but in general she was friendly. I was a little unnerved as Pete drove firstly to her place to drop her off - bypassing my house. I sat quietly in the back seat, wondering if I would be safe with these two men I had only just met, when I heard Billy say,

'Don't worry we are dropping you off next.' He smiled reassuringly and I relaxed a little.

On arrival at 202, Billy got out of the car to escort me to my door.

'Are you putting the kettle on?'

I saw Pete's car pull off so, being the trusting person I am, I didn't see the harm in one cup of coffee. So I agreed, thinking his friend had gone. While making the drink, the kitchen door opened and in walked Pete, which startled me.

'I thought you had gone,' I said firmly as my nerves returned, but his happy demeanour and friendly attitude soon eased me.

Pete looked around for Billy and realised he was sitting in the next room. Without being asked, he walked through the door and joined him. I could hear the two of them chatting very quietly which slightly perturbed me; I quietly stood behind the door in order to listen to their conversation.

'Two's up?'

I recognised Pete's voice. Naively I didn't understand what he meant. I was intrigued to hear how Billy would reply, hoping to understand the comment. With the mugs of coffee in my hands I stood just out of sight. I heard Billy reply,

'No, not this one, she's special.'

I felt myself relax, feeling a little more secure as it dawned on me they were referring to sex. I entered the room with the coffee but stayed near the door in order to run if need be. The conversation flowed and I began to enjoy their company. After he had finished his coffee, Pete made his excuses and left. I must admit I was pleased to see him go, thus leaving Billy and me with the night before us.

I didn't feel threatened by Billy - on the contrary - he had a calming way about him. 'Where's your daughter?' Billy asked after seeing her framed photograph on the wall. He put his mug down and moved towards me.

'At her dad's.'

He sat close beside me and took hold of my hand.

'You're a very pretty lady,' he said with a glint in his eye.

'So I've been told, but thank you anyway,' I shyly said, thoroughly embarrassed.

'Seriously,' he smiled 'I can't believe I haven't seen you before. Where have you been hiding?'

'I don't go out much. I have my little girl to think about and I'm going through a divorce so I'm just getting my life back together.'

By this time he had begun kissing me gently on my shoulder which made my whole body tremble with expectation. I resisted his attempts to convince me to go to the bedroom but his charms began to work and although nervous we ended up in my single bed. He was sensual and tender and his demeanour was kind and caring. I hadn't slept with anyone as gentle before. He made me feel good about myself and I realised I had been missing the touch of a man, one who put me first in lovemaking. I woke in the morning held in his arms. I didn't feel cheap for giving in to his attentions and he made me feel special. I felt happy. That morning Pete arrived to pick Billy up for their day's activities and I made them a cup of tea.

'She's even more beautiful without make-up on, isn't she Billy?' Pete remarked as he took his cup from me. I blushed again with embarrassment.

'She is, so different to the usual slags around here.'

I looked at him feeling a little awkward, especially after I had slept with him. He must have realised I didn't like his comment, so a wink and a smile came my way, which made me smile to myself and I forgave him. Before they left, Billy asked for my telephone number. I wrote it down for him and he left giving me a gentle kiss on the cheek.

I didn't hear from him for a few days; deep down I was hoping he would ring. I didn't go out the following Saturday night as money was tight and with Anna's fifth birthday looming - I had promised her a party with her newly made friends from school. Christmas was only a few weeks away, so I decided going out was a low priority. The following Sunday, eight days after my evening with Billy, a knock rapped on the door around 7.30pm. Anna was tucked up in bed and I was alone watching television. Surprised but pleased, I opened the door to see Billy.

'Hi,' he said with a glint in his eye and a cheeky grin on his face.

'Come in,' I invited, hiding the fact I was very pleased to see him.

'Just came to see if you're okay. I looked for you last night but you didn't come in the pub. I lost your phone number and thought I would wait 'til I saw you out, not wanting to impose by coming to your door. Are you alone?' As he spoke I noticed his eyes were scanning around the living room. Though I thought his inspection of my home when he visited me was a little strange, it didn't occur it was the house he wanted and he intended moving in and taking it from under me.

'I am, as usual,' I replied with a smile.

'Well I'm not stopping, just thought I'd come and say hello, see you haven't gone off me. I'm off out with Pete so I'll get going and hopefully see you soon.' He walked slowly as he left, looking around as he got to the door.

'Is your daughter in bed?'

'She is; I won't be out for a while,' I said. 'I have got too many commitments. But here's my number again, ring me. Maybe you could down one evening?'

He liked that idea and said he would ring in a few days. Leaving, he gently kissed me on my cheek. He presented himself as polite and being quite the gentleman, and although we slept together that first night, I didn't feel under any pressure and I was sure he didn't think of me as cheap. It wasn't something I would normally do and I had heard him say to Pete I was special, so there was no reason to rush into anything. After all, I had Anna to think about.

Eventually the phone call came, a week later on the Sunday teatime. Billy asked if it was convenient to come down that evening. I said it would but he should make it after 8pm, after I had got Anna settled for the night. That didn't appear to be a problem to him. He arrived around 8.15pm and I was looking forward to having some adult company. He'd bought a bottle of wine for me and some beers for himself, saying he didn't like wine. He seemed quite a thoughtful man. We watched television and chatted about ourselves, trying to get to know each other a little more. It was a lovely evening and with a few gentle kisses flowing, it seemed romantic. He left at around 11.30pm asking if I would like to go out with him on a date the following Saturday night. I accepted his invitation, but told him it was the afternoon of Anna's party so I wasn't sure what time I would be available.

'That's OK. I'll come down for you around 8.30pm. That should give you plenty of time.'

I smiled in agreement and he left, leaving the usual kissed cheek. I felt happy. I had met what seemed like a responsible, kind, considerate man who wanted nothing from me except for a little of my time; this felt good after the possessive, jealous husband I was divorcing.

Saturday soon came round and Anna was excited when her friends started to arrive. I could see the pleasure on her face. Anna had found her parents' split a little hard at times and her behaviour was sometimes a little erratic; she was at last settling down and beginning to enjoy her new life with her mummy. Giving me the benefit of her motherly experience, mum helped with Anna whenever she could. Anna's worries were far away and her fifth birthday was panning out to be a good one. During the party, mum and I were in the kitchen putting the jelly and ice cream into individual dishes and having a break from the party games and the noise of eleven excited boys and girls screeching with excitement.

'Would you be able to have Anna tonight for me, mum? A friend has asked me out and I would like to go but can't afford a babysitter.'

My request was happily granted mum said she would take her down home with them when dad came to pick her up. On saying I would pick her up in time to go to her dad's next day, but dad said to get her clothes ready and he would take her to her mamma Hazel's; all I had to do was ring Hazel and let her know the plan. Mark always went to his mum's on Sunday morning before picking Anna up, so it would save him the journey to my place. I thanked my parents as they left and hugged Anna goodbye. Skipping up the path, she happily got in the car with my parents. We waved as the car pulled away and blew kisses to each other until she disappeared out of sight. I ran excitedly into the house and straight upstairs. While the bath was filling with the sweet aroma of scented bubble bath, I quickly tidied my bedroom (just in case as Anna was staying at mum's) choosing my clothes carefully; a nice top and jeans. I placed the make-up I was going to use on my dressing table. Switching my curling tongs and hairdryer on, I made the decision to curl my long blonde hair that night. When all was prepared I got into the hot bubbly bath water. Relaxing in the heat of the water, I went through the day's events. Smiling at the thought of Anna's happiness of the day and having her friends round; pleased with myself for having saved to give her a special day. My attentions turned to the date I had that night, which again brought a big smile to my face: this time it was my excitement. I lay there until the water began to cool and then moved into my bedroom to prepare to meet the new man in my life, oblivious to the life he was setting me up to endure. He arrived just after 8pm.

'Sorry I'm a little early, hope you don't mind,' he said as his eyes looked around the room. 'Are you alone?'

'Yes, Anna has gone to my parents' for the night, so I'm all yours.' He smiled and with a warm hug, he kissed me.

'I'm almost ready; just got to get my bag,' I said, popping into the hallway where my handbag was hidden under a coat. We set off walking to the local where we had met, chatting and laughing about the events of Anna's party. I walked into the pub where I saw a few people I knew and was drawn into various conversations, during which someone asked if I was seeing Billy. I said that I was, but the response was to deflate my happy demeanour.

'You must be mad.'

I couldn't understand this attitude and then I noticed that people were staring at us. Quietly, I asked Billy why people didn't seem happy we were together.

'They're probably jealous - you are a beautiful lady and you're with me. Don't worry about what people think or say.' He smiled, winked and hugged me with his arm around my waist.

We continued to drink and enjoy the evening. Feeling happy and relaxed, we talked and laughed. Billy stayed the night and he was pleasant and attentive.

'While you were in the bathroom I borrowed some money out of your change jar and nipped over to the shop for some cigarettes hope that's alright,' he mentioned as he prepared to leave in the morning. I smiled and it didn't worry me: after all, he had paid for the night out and I didn't begrudge him a bit of change. It didn't occur to me to wonder why he hadn't any money left from the previous night. As he left he kissed my cheek tenderly, saying he would ring me.

The next time we met I told him that I had organised a party on Boxing Day.

'Oh, that's the day our family have a party all day and night; I was hoping you would come this year.'

Having invited a lot of friends I said,

'I can't let my friends down now, it's been planned all year and I'm looking forward to it. I was determined not to cancel my party. There was a stony silence between us.

'If you can't come, don't worry. I'll see you sometime during Christmas - but I'm at my parents' on Christmas Day.'

He said he would get away from his parents' party for an hour in the evening and pop down; this seemed a good compromise.

Boxing Day arrived and Anna left to go to her daddy's to enjoy their time together. She was stopping over for two nights which was really helpful, with having party plans. No sooner had she left when three of my friends arrived to help with the cooking and preparations for the night's party. This was so different to the previous Christmas where I had spent most of it alone, other than the Christmas Day meal where I joined my parents and family. That had been a good day but I'd left around 7pm. It had been a lonely walk home and I'd glanced into the windows of the houses we passed on the way. I saw families enjoying the festivities, with their paper hats from Christmas crackers lodged precariously on their heads. Laughter seemed to drift from one house into another. I realised that Christmas had never been the same since I left home after marrying Mark. Our Christmases consisted of him getting drunk and becoming sarcastic and causing arguments, especially if he was in the company of my family. Holding Anna's hand tightly, we steadily walked through the snow heading for 202. On arrival home, Anna and I had spent time playing with her new gifts and chatting about the exciting time she would have with her daddy the next day. I'd put Anna to bed and returned downstairs, determined next year would be different. I had sat in the quiet of the house. I had no television or even a radio; my only entertainment other than my daughter was a record player lent to me by my friend Beth on which I could play the precious records I had collected since I was twelve-years-old. Reaching for a pen and a note pad, I'd decided I had to take control of my life and make plans for the future. I was determined to have a better year by the following Christmas, hence the organised party.

All my wishes had come true. I had been in college since September after enrolling onto the RSA course to update my office skills. I had been sitting in at night, learning French from a book borrowed from the local library. Reconnecting with friends who had been neglected due to Mark's jealous and possessive nature had enabled me to have a social life - most of all; I had met a lovely, gentle man who seemed to adore me. I had decorated and refurnished my home, replacing and returning some of the donated furniture from the volunteer bureau - which had helped me when I moved into the house with nothing. Mark and I were now friends after the bitterness of the break-up. Life was looking good for me at last.

The girls and I had fun all day with the party preparations, drinking and listening to the latest hits on the radio/cassette player. When everything was set up, we got dressed in our glad-rags and set off to meet friends in town, inviting even more people along the way. By the time we got to 202 at 11pm we were all in party mood. Around midnight, my parents walked in.

'Are we invited?' Mum asked with a smile.

'Of course you are; I'm really happy you came,' I replied, proud as punch.

At 2am, Billy walked in. Surprised that the party was still full of revellers, he gave me a kiss and I introduced him to my parents. Leaving them chatting I resumed dancing with my friends. Within ten minutes, he had convinced them to accompany him to his house to meet his parents and have a drink: they gladly accepted and said their goodbyes. The night went without any problems and everyone seemed to have a good time. It was about 8am by the time everyone had left and I started to clear up. I knew I had the rest of the day to sleep, so I'd started picking up glasses and taking them into the kitchen when a knock rapped on the door around 8.30am. It was Billy.

'Come to help clear up?' I jokingly asked.

'Your mess; you clean it,' he snapped. 'What time did they all leave. Or is someone still upstairs?'

I didn't like what he was implying and I told him so. I had a handful of glasses and slammed them down on the kitchen table in temper, breaking two of them. Shards of glass fell onto me, cutting and sticking into my leg just above my left knee.

'Ouch,' I winced, as I sat on the nearest chair. He shot over to me and gently picked up my knee, resting my foot on his lap, he had kneeled on the floor before me.

'Look what you've done to yourself, temper gets you nowhere.'

He carefully removed any shards protruding from my skin and with a damp towel he wrapped my knee to stem the bleeding.

'I didn't mean anything by it,' he mumbled, not lifting his head.

That was to be the forerunner to his sadistic, manipulative, controlling behaviour. When he eventually lifted his head, his eyes met mine. They had changed colour from blue to a bright intense green, something that was to eventually teach me to beware. Billy must have mistaken my puzzled look for one of annoyance because he advised:

'Leave the cleaning up. You're tired. You go to bed for a while. This will wait; I'll pop down later.' He hurriedly kissed my cheek and left.

I was to realise it was too soon at that time - to show his real self.

I locked the door behind him. He was right I was very tired, exhausted in fact. I limped up the stairs to my room and I'm

26

sure I was asleep before my head hit the pillow. I finally woke up as it was getting dark outside; I had slept all day, sleeping off the alcohol and the exhaustion. I lay for a while thinking about the party, and how nice it was for my parents to pop in. Then it dawned on me they went to Billy's house and I hadn't even met his family yet. I wondered what their verdict was going to be. Somebody rapped on the door. My friend Beth had arrived to see if the tidying up had been done or if I needed help, which was nice and appreciated. As we cleaned up she asked what had happened to my knee, so I told her how I had cut it. In disbelief she asked:

'You're sure that's how it happened?'

I assured her I wasn't lying, why should I?

'So are you and Billy seeing each other permanently now?'

'It looks like it,' I answered, thinking her questions a little intrusive.

'You know he's Dave Burnshaw's brother - don't you?'

'No actually I didn't. I met him at the Star Inn a few weeks ago. I had never seen him before then. Why, do you know him?' Turning the questions on to her.

'I know of him,' she replied, not looking at me.

No more was spoken about Billy but the awkward silence troubled me. We had almost finished the cleaning and were preparing to settle down for a girl's night in when a knock came on the door. It was Billy.

'You feel any better?'

As he walked into the living room, he and Beth looked at each other.

'Right then, I'll be off,' said Beth.

'No, Beth, I thought we were going to have a drink.' I wanted her to stay but she wouldn't.

'Another time hey?' She grabbed her coat and made her way to the door. Her quick exit worried me. I asked Billy if he knew her. He didn't but said to forget about it. We talked about the night's events and I asked how he got on with my parents. Though he said my mum and dad were pleased to meet his parents and that everyone got on, something seemed a little odd in his manner. He didn't seem to want to talk about it, so I didn't push it and we settled down to a night watching the television and relaxed. He left early next morning.

Anna came back the following evening escorted by her daddy; she seemed very happy but tired. Mark came in to look at all her gifts from Santa and to bring in the ones Santa had left at his family's house. He sat for a while and joined me for a cup of tea.

'Can I ask you a question?' Mark asked quite cautiously.

'Sure, but I may not answer it.' He did tend to think I was still answerable to him, even though he was engaged to someone else. As a husband he had been possessive, so I never liked it when he asked if he could ask me a question. I liked the fact we were friends if only for Anna's sake - so I didn't want to upset him. He started nervously to ask:

'I have heard something that has worried me a little.'

I sat listening to what he had to say, wondering what was coming next. It certainly wasn't what I expected.

'You're seeing someone called Billy, aren't you?'

'Yes, what of it?'

'Do you know he is very violent?'

'Don't be daft,' I snapped. 'You don't know him.'

'I do. Be careful Jeannie - he has a bad reputation.'

He realised I wasn't happy with what he had said to me, so he slightly smiled and kissed Anna goodbye as he headed off to continue his evening. I put Anna to bed and filled it with her new teddies and dolls to keep her company. Kissing her goodnight, I returned to the living room, to take in what Mark had told me. Billy had been nothing but a gentleman and polite; he wasn't rushing to move into my house or to meet Anna, so I couldn't understand why Mark said what he had. I decided to discuss it with Billy the next time I saw him. He usually came for a few hours most nights after Anna had gone to bed, only staying when Anna was at my mum's or her dad's overnight. He arrived as expected and after the normal greetings and chat I began to broach the subject.

'Mark said something tonight that has worried me a little,' I said, trying not to make a big deal of it.

'Oh yeah, and what might that be? Don't tell me, he said I'm a nasty piece of work.' I noticed a little sarcasm in his voice.

'You're violent, apparently.'

'Yeah, okay,' he said as his sarcasm increased. 'Why because I don't take crap from anyone?'

I sat quiet, taking in what he was saying, but he didn't seem to show any meanness or nastiness and I thought all the gossip and interference would turn anyone a little sarcastic.

'Look, we have been seeing each other a few weeks now; have I ever done anything or said anything to frighten you?'

'No,' I replied, because he hadn't.

'There you are then, just take no notice. It's because I got locked up once. There was a big fight in town a few years ago, but I was the only one who got sent down for it. I would never hit a woman.'

Naively I believed him.

'Come here,' he said, as he sidled up next to me and kissed me. 'I could never hurt you.

You are lovely,' he whispered as he got a little amorous.

I smiled and stupidly chose to believe Billy's story: I hadn't had any reason to think it wasn't true. A few days later I introduced him to Anna. He was good with her, spoiling her with gifts and sweets when he came to visit; she liked him and was happy when he was around. Eventually Billy was staying over most nights. As he was working, he would take us out at the weekend, both Anna and I. We were enjoying him being in our lives.

A few weeks later when I went to visit mum she asked:

'Can I tell you something without upsetting you?'

'Of course,' I replied, wondering why mum worried about upsetting me. When mum had something to say she said it, hang the consequences. With a slightly nervous expression she began.

'We were out in town last night and when we went into the chip shop, a woman came up to me and your dad, she asked if we were your parents. When I said yes she said, "You ought to warn her that Billy she's seeing is violent he nearly killed his last partner. I'd be worried if I was you". Then she walked off. Don't ask me who she was or why she said it, but she was obviously concerned.'

'Jealous, more like,' I said under my breath. After a cold silence between mum and me, I sensed she wished she had never said anything and so did I. I answered her worries, hoping to put them to rest.

'Mum, he's so nice to us, both of us: yes he told me he has been prison for fighting but that was men, it wasn't for hitting women.'

'Well I'm just telling you what she said and we weren't very happy at their house on Boxing night: they're too common - swearing and falling out. We didn't stay long. Even your dad said, "Well I hope she doesn't stay with this one for very long".' She finished by saying, 'They really aren't our type of people.'

I didn't enter into a conversation about it. Billy had assured me he wasn't that type of person and I foolishly decided not to listen to her or anyone else. Nothing else was said about the subject, as mum didn't want to cause a rift between us. For the rest of the visit we chatted about other things and spent time playing with Anna, though the subdued atmosphere was clearly apparent. When I saw Billy I tried to discuss what mum had said, but all he said was:

'I'm not listening to tittle tattle or gossip. If you believe what they say, then I will leave now and you can find someone else for them to call.'

I didn't want him to leave he had ended my loneliness and made us happy. I got on well with his family, especially Dave - we had been friends for years. Billy had never shown any inkling of violence towards me, so I decided not to listen to gossip either. Life continued happily. He went out all day to work and I had time to myself during the day, with Anna being at school. Eventually he stayed every night officially moving in when I told the council (though the council officer warned me not to put him on the rent book. I couldn't understand why but fortunately I did heed his advice). Happily we continued to live our lives together.

My sisters-in-law, Ellen and Julia, were both expecting their first babies which brought home to me the reality of the fact I was subconsciously still mourning the death of Thomas, my stillborn son. I realised at this point I was desperately yearning for a baby. The subject often arose and Billy and I would talk about it and imagine what he or she would look like. Even though we hadn't been together very long, the feeling of love and security in this relationship had deepened. We spent most of our time together, whether it was out and about with Anna, or in the garden tending to the vegetables, or just pottering around the house. It was the closeness of a family I had fallen in love with after a previous marriage of loneliness, isolation and the indifference of a selfish man. Anna seemed very important to him. He spent time with her teaching her to read and write; they would laugh together and she seemed very happy and contented around him. Marriage wasn't an option as I was still married to Mark. This turned out to be a blessing in disguise. We had begun proceedings for a divorce on the grounds of irretrievable breakdown; that way, neither of us got the blame. I had been far too young at the age of seventeen to get married, but life at home had begun to be intolerable, having let my family down by falling pregnant. So for now, I was content to live with Billy in my little council house.

I knew Billy liked to drink and sometimes it would be quite heavily, but I never saw anything to suggest that we would be in danger, like the gossips had implied. Quite the opposite: he was funny and seemed intent on making his new family the centre of his world. Little did I realise this was all part of Billy's plan.

I saw my family regularly. Knowing my parents didn't approve of him, Billy kept his distance, but never interfered with my visits and there was never any atmosphere on my return home. Again the subject of us having a baby arose one evening and we decided that the time was right; we didn't want there to be too many years between Anna and the new baby. The following May I realised I had missed two periods and went to visit my doctor. It was a very tense time for me personally: after Thomas. I was afraid it would happen again. I had told Billy all about my previous pregnancy and how awful it was at the birth, having had a full-term baby. He seemed to understand my fears. With the reassurance he would take care of me and wouldn't let the doctors do anything I didn't want them to, I began to feel calmer. I believed in him. By the time I had left the doctor's I was confident that with Dr Wright looking after me, and Billy by my side, it would be fine and I would be able to have another baby. The confirmation test went off from the doctor's to the hospital and I had to wait one week to see if the results were positive. It was an anxious week. Each day dragged while Anna was at school and Billy at work. We kept it to ourselves, so as not to tempt fate. I couldn't talk to anyone about how I was feeling. Soon the day arrived. Billy went off to work nervously that morning as he anticipated becoming a father.

'I'll ring you at lunchtime,' he said, as he glanced back at me while opening the door. His smile said everything I needed to see. He was happy. I knew he would be on tenterhooks all morning, wondering if the test would be positive. I got Anna ready for school and tried to go about my daily routine, putting the thoughts of the call I had to make that morning out of my mind. I sat in the chair beside the telephone for a few minutes, trying to summon up courage to make the call to the surgery. I inhaled a deep breath and with mixed feelings I dialled the number. I gave my name and why I was calling and waited for the results. I felt sick with trepidation. Whether it was because I was frightened of a repeat pregnancy, or people thinking I was replacing Thomas or anything else I didn't know; I couldn't stop the sick feeling as I awaited the outcome of the results.

'Hi,' said the receptionist. 'Yes, it's positive, so please make an appointment with Dr Wright as soon as possible.'

I sat quietly for a while, letting the news sink in. Soon I started to smile and feel excited. From that moment on this little baby growing inside me was loved. I silently spoke to Thomas,

'This baby will never make me forget you - you will always be my missing son and I will carry you in my heart.'

It was a long wait until Billy came home at 5pm. I saw him get out of the truck at the bus stop across the road. His face was sporting a big grin. I knew he had told his work-mates by the expression on the driver's face. He ran across the road towards the little green gate, slamming it shut behind him. I rushed to the door to greet him. Picking me up and kissing me while swinging me around was a great response. We were so happy. Anna began laughing and dancing around us with all the excitement, not knowing why we were so happy. Once we had calmed a little, we asked Anna to sit down as we had something to tell her. I explained that she was going to have a baby brother or sister. She stood up and hugged me, putting her arms around me.

'Will it be like last time, mummy?'

I knew she was referring to me going into hospital; she was still a little confused where our Thomas was. Too young to understand: all she knew was Thomas was living in heaven with Jesus.

'Well, darling, I'm hoping this time I can bring the baby home from the hospital and it can live with us.'

'Can I tell daddy?' she asked, joining in the excitement and happiness.

We asked her to wait a while, though when we were ready to announce the pregnancy she could be the one to tell him. Anna smiled as the news sank in. She ran to Billy, who was patiently listening to our conversation. She hugged him and as children do, went off to play with her toys as if nothing had happened.

I smiled to myself as I felt my life was going well - everything was happening fast, but it was all good. I was to have a baby with someone who would really be there for me and that was worth everything. Meeting Billy had taken away all the sadness that had scarred my young life. Soon into the pregnancy, I started showing the defined bump that gives away the secret, so the decision to tell our families was made. Of course my parents weren't going to be happy because they didn't like Billy. So my news wasn't going to be received as happily as my brothers' announcements the previous Christmas. On that occasion the congratulations and exuberance made for a happy day and although I was very pleased and excited for both brothers and their wives - deep down there was sadness - my news was never going to be so happily received.

But even though I had had two pregnancies - which both had caused problems, I was determined not to listen to the negative comments. I intended to enjoy this one. I deserved to.

8.10pm September 20th.

'Are you okay in there?' Mum's concern showed in her voice as she knocked on the bathroom door.

'Yes, sorry, did you want the bathroom?'

'No, just making sure you are alright. I have just made some tea if you want some.' She spoke softly and her gentleness bought tears to my eyes.

'Okay,' I answered not realising how long I had been lying in the water.

My skin had crinkled as the water had cooled. I had lost track of time in my peaceful recollections of happier times. I was trying to make some sense of what had happened to me. The stiffness of my limbs caused me to struggle as I began to climb out of the bath. I quickly covered myself up in a large soft white bath towel which only served to exaggerate the paleness of my skin. I tried not to see the bruises on my body as I dried myself, dabbing the towel lightly around the painful areas of fresh, pale-blue skin which linked up the purple, black and browns of the established healing lumps and bruises which, over the months and weeks, had joined forces to change the overall appearance of my body. I found a new toothbrush in the cabinet and knew no-one would mind me taking it. Carefully opening my mouth, I attempted to clean my teeth. I could see the swelling around my neck turning blue after the redness had calmed down and blending with the bruising which was creeping up towards my left cheek. I wondered how I was going to hide this from my parents. I lowered the toothbrush and stared at the injury through the small cabinet mirror. I held onto the sink to steady myself and my hands shook as tears trickled from my eyes. Soon the trickle turned into gushes as it dawned on me I was away from the man who was hell-bent on crushing me. My cries were loud and uncontrollable; with each deep sob my body vibrated with pain etched deep within. For Lilly's sake I had to be strong and see our escape through, but I wasn't strong: I was weak, so very weak. My cries eventually subsided, leaving a scarred face and soul in the mirror sorrowfully returning my gaze. Reaching for a towel, I patted my face carefully, took a deep breath and composed myself. Giving in to emotional outbursts wasn't the norm for me anymore, but this was the first sight of the result of what the last two years had done to me. I wasn't given to feeling sorry for myself; throughout the beatings it was always the sense of survival that took over in a desperate attempt to protect my daughters, but for a split second an expression of pity replaced my usual stoic appearance. My pity soon disappeared as I thought about the future. How was I going to protect my daughter from such a monster? What I didn't realise then, or for the next two years, was that I would be in a court of law facing a prison sentence.

Returning downstairs I was conscious of my parents looking at each other as they watched me struggle with a drink of tea. Knowing they had seen the severity of the hand-marks around my neck, I silently stared into my cup. They must have heard my sobs in the bathroom.

'Do you think you could eat anything yet?' mum's gentle sympathetic voice asked. 'You're so thin. I'm so worried about you: just try a little more salad if nothing else.'

Slowly I managed to eat a little ham and tomatoes, mum's occasional discreet side-glances assuring me of her concern. I ate enough to appease her, after which I returned upstairs to Lilly, who was soundly sleeping. I didn't want to be away from her for long, needing to be there if she woke. Gently I lay on the bed next to her, curling gently around her. I watched her eyelids flickering, hoping her dreams were sweet ones. Listening to her serene breathing comforted me; my eyes wandered over to the old window which, as a child, I looked out of a million times. The autumn sun began to fade and the distinct scent of the night air drifted slowly through the opened sash. I couldn't relax my mind which was on hyper mode, waiting for the imminent appearance of Billy: only on this occasion, I knew it would be a fight over Lilly. In his eyes she belonged to him, she was his possession. In my anxiety, I made my way to the window looking across the park. I reassured myself of Billy's absence. Closing the window a little, leaving it slightly ajar, I moved quietly and kissed my sleeping baby goodnight. Taking one last look back, I closed the door. I hoped I had enough strength to see this night through. A feeling of foreboding was creeping slowly into my mind.

On entering the living room I could smell aftershave; I followed the odour into the kitchen. To my despair, I saw dad dressed up and shaved in preparation to go out for the evening. I felt my heart sink as the trembling returned.

'Dad,' I said, shocked, 'you're not going out, are you?'

He sensed the panic in my voice.

'He won't come down here. I've told you before - you are safe here.'

'Dad he will, I know him. This isn't the end - he won't let us go this easily.' My voice panicky, I continued. 'As soon as he's been to his mam's and we aren't there he will come here.'

'Stop worrying,' he said, as he pushed by me and picked up his car keys. 'Your mum's got people coming down soon, so you won't be on your own.'

That did nothing to reassure me; in fact I felt worse knowing mum would be shown up in front of her guests. As dad left I ran to the six-foot wooden gate, bolting it in panic, as I worried that mum could get hurt. I began to regret coming here. Putting mum in this danger was the last thing I thought would happen; naturally I thought dad would protect me, but he had gone. Despondent and frightened, I sat down by the table astonished at dad's attitude. Soon mum arrived from the kennel area and came in to the kitchen, where she saw me looking pensive.

'Dad's gone out, mum. What are we going to do when Billy comes down?'

'He wouldn't dare, not with all these dogs here,' she said with a slight grin on her face. 'Come on Jeannie, he would be an idiot to come here.'

I felt like no-one was taking me seriously. I began to feel impending doom. I knew him: they did not. No-one knew the ferocity of his violence. I heard the gate rattle and my stomach turned somersaults. I couldn't stand - my legs wouldn't let me – and my trembling increased as fear gripped me.

'Hello, you found us OK?' Mum's voice appeared calm. For a split second I thought it was Billy she was talking to but soon realised he wouldn't be greeted with that tone. Peering around the opened door, I saw her unbolting the gate. As her guests entered I felt my sickness turn into relief. They greeted me as they walked through into the living room. Trying to be useful, I put the kettle on to make tea for mum's guests. After which - I nipped up to check on Lilly. I knew she was safe and sleeping but my mind wouldn't settle. I needed to see her.

8.55pm September 20th.

Dad had been gone for around twenty minutes and I had heard mum chattering with her guests. I decided to return downstairs after regaining my composure. The visitors were a couple interested in buying a puppy from the kennel. They had obviously sensed I was a little nervous about something, they were very friendly towards me but I couldn't afford to let my guard down. Mum nipped up to the kennels to return the puppy to its siblings. It hadn't occurred to me that the T-shirt I was wearing was loose around my neck and was showing the hand-mark bruising around my throat. I noticed the look of sympathy come over the visiting lady's face during a conversation; she had noticed the bruising, which instantly threw me into embarrassment. I shrugged my shoulder upwards while lowering my chin into my chest in order to disguise the full extent of my injury. I fiddled constantly with my hair in the vain attempt to cover the marks on the side of my cheek. Usually, I was kept out of sight until the bruising had healed, so it didn't occur to me to hide away. I heard the gate open: it had obviously been left unlocked after the guests arrived. I was slightly relieved because it broke the atmosphere occurring in the living room. I turned to head for the door to see who had entered the gate and to my horror Billy was standing before me. The fury on his face matched the evilness in his eyes as they shone a bright intimidating green. I swallowed deeply. I couldn't speak, my eyes fixed on those of my abuser. Alcohol emanated from his breath as his panting spewed out the smell of stale drink and cigarettes. My stomach turned as I recognised the ever-familiar stench that preceded the usual verbal obscenities.

'Where is she?' He shoved by me, barging into the living room to the startled guests.

'Upstairs asleep,' my mind frantically thought what to do.

'Fetch her, now!' he bellowed, his tone menacing and rude.

The visiting couple sat riveted in their seats, watching and listening to what was happening.

'Okay,' I meekly said in compliance. 'It'll take me a few minutes to get her things together.'

Forcing my legs to move I left the room, shutting the adjoining door to the stairs hoping he wouldn't follow me. There wasn't time to think clearly but, instead of going to collect Lilly from upstairs, I found myself running as fast but as quietly as possible outside to find mum.

'Mum,' my voice quivering and breathless.

'Yes I'm here,' she said, as I heard the familiar greeting of happy barking and whining dogs.

'Billy's in the house.'

She recognised the urgency of my statement.

'Where does he think you are?'

'Upstairs, fetching Lilly,' I replied, finding it difficult to keep calm.

'Good thinking: now go up to your room and lock yourself in. Drag the wardrobe in front of the door and be as quiet as you can. Promise me no matter what he does or what you hear, you won't come out of the room. Try to keep Lilly quiet - he doesn't know the house, so it will take time for him to find you. Go on, do as I say.' She turned me around and with a gentle push she repeated:

'Go.'

I returned as quietly as I could down the path and into the stairs door. Carefully I hurried up the stairs, my heart thumping as it echoed in my ears with each gentle tread on the wooden steps. I hadn't time to panic or think. I did as I was told. I reached the bedroom door, where I stepped as cautiously as possible onto the wooden floor which was directly above the living room. I slid the wardrobe in front of the door, which made a screeching sound as it slid across the floorboards. Panic set in as I feared the sound would alert Billy to where we were. I covered my mouth as the sounds of terror-cries started to slowly appear. I crept to the window to breathe in fresh air in the hope of subduing my cries.

'You will have to go through me to get to her again.' Mum's voice sounded firm but calm.

'That's no problem - you fucking whore. Where's my kid?'

'Get backside that gate Billy or I will let the dogs out.'

'Daddy,' cried Lilly. 'Daddy, daddy,' she had been woken by the commotion.

I quickly got to Lilly and lifted her into my arms. Curling up on the bed, tears streamed down our terrified faces. I worried for mum's safety. Lilly wriggled to get free as she repeated her cries for her daddy. I placed my hand across her mouth in order to stop her shouts for him. She went quiet as we heard the scuffling outside under our window. Everything seemed to go silent for a while then I heard the male visitor threaten to ring the police. 'Please, please,' I thought, 'please ring them.' I was getting more anxious about mum being in danger.

'Ring them. Do you think I'm afraid of them fucking twats?' Billy's belligerent manner directed towards the man.

A sudden smash of a glass milk bottle startled me. I sneaked to the window, standing back from the window so Billy couldn't see me, hoping to see what was happening, but Lilly's cries forced me to return to her. I began to sing a little song to her in the hope of blocking out the noise and soothing her. Over my nervous singing I heard mum yelling.

'Go on then - you coward. I'm not Jeannette. I'm not scared of you. Go on. You woman beater - see if you dare.'

'Mum,' I thought, 'please don't goad him. He will hurt you.'

A scream came from the lady visitor. I rushed to the bedroom door. I knew I had to help mum. I was just about to push the wardrobe away from the door when I remembered what she said: 'no matter what you hear, don't come out'. She was trying to protect me. I didn't know what to do. To put her through this and ignore her orders would show a lack of respect, but to ignore the fact she was in danger would haunt me if anything happened to her. I turned to look at Lilly; frantically I wondered what to do. Her little eyes told me to stay with her - she needed my protection as much as I needed my mother's.

'Right, I warned you.' I heard mum's angry voice as it grew louder. I heard her footsteps heading up the garden path.

'I'm not leaving here without my fucking kid. She can go to hell. But that kid's mine.' Billy was raving and ranting now, knowing his bullying wasn't working on mum.

I heard the growl of the dogs as they ran down the path towards the intruder intent on harming their owner. The gate quickly opened, then slammed shut. The dogs continued jumping up at the six-foot gate while Billy's obscenities were screamed at mum. I felt ashamed. I heard mum shut the kitchen door, leaving the dogs to defend their territory. Within a few minutes I saw the flashing of blue lights and heard the sirens of police cars howling down the street. Dogs were barking, Billy was shouting and Lilly was crying; it was mayhem. Trying to shield Lilly from this was almost impossible, but I knew she had heard worse in her young life. I cradled her in my arms and forced myself to sing an unconvincing lullaby. My throat was dry and hurting, but Lilly needed me to be calm, which in turn calmed her. Rocking her slowly, I placed my little finger in her hand. I felt her fingers wrap around it. Singing into her ear took effect, still sniffling, her tears sparkled as the blue lights shone through the room. Eventually she drifted off into her dreams. I heard the kitchen door open and mum order 'Toro' and 'Nero' to be quiet. They instantly ceased their barking but continued to growl at the gate, warning the intruder not to attempt to re-enter.

'Can you secure your dogs, please madam?' asked one of the policemen.

'In', she ordered. I heard them rush into the house, allowing the policeman to enter the gate. Everything except for the slamming of car doors went quiet. I strained my ears to listen to the muffled voices below in the living room. Soon the kitchen door was opened and out ran the dogs, followed by the policeman and mum, after which the police cars disappeared taking the offensive man with them. Walking over to the window, I saw mum returning the excited animals back to their respective kennels and apologising to her guests. By now they understood the reason for my facial bruises. They left soon after making another appointment to visit at a later date. I waited for mum to shout up at me; she didn't. I felt a coward hiding and letting mum deal with violence. I waited upstairs listening to the clattering of pots in the kitchen, wondering why she hadn't fetched me. Thoughts of guilt riddled my mind as I felt the ever growing shame of the situation. Eventually I heard footsteps climbing the stairs and a faint knock on the bedroom door.

'You're safe now, the kettle's on,' she whispered through the closed door. Mum waited until she heard me slide the wardrobe from the door, and then made her way downstairs. I made sure Lilly was sleeping, then followed mum into the living room.

'I'm so sorry, mum.'

'Nothing's your fault Jeannie. Here, drink this.'

'Lord above - is that what you have been living under? He is a raving madman, no wonder you're terrified. Well he doesn't scare me. The police said to warn you he is asleep at the moment on the sofa. They had to return him to your house because that's where he is registered to be living. They advise us he will probably return once he wakes up. Under no circumstances are you to see him or speak to him, because it will ignite the situation. They also suggest you seek legal advice in regards to Lilly and regaining your house. So I hope you're fit for a fight, because on what I've seen tonight he won't give up easily'.'

I couldn't reply to her. I sat in fear, shame and exhaustion. Shortly afterwards I went upstairs to the bedroom. I knew I wouldn't sleep, but I needed time alone. I put a small chair beside the window. I could see Lilly while at the same time watch outside for Billy's re-appearance. As Lilly slept, I thought about the hell which was our life.

The Eyes of a Monster

It was a warm Friday night in the August of 1983 when I first saw the eyes of a monster. The aroma of sweet blossom and roses filled the air as we walked home together after a night out with Billy's parents. The local team was short of a domino player and I was asked to make up the numbers. I wasn't very keen but I decided not to let everyone down and as Billy was partnering me I knew he could guide the game so we would win, which he did. After a successful evening, the time came to make our way home. His parents decided that, as it was a lovely summer night, they would join us for the walk home. A short while after we began our journey, his father asked me a question that threw me a little.

'Dave says you're good girl - you are a good girl, aren't you?'

I took it to mean 'am I faithful and honest' so I replied,

'Yes I am,' giving him a little smile.

'Do you promise me you are?'

.'I promise,' I answered, a little surprised, adding the gentle laugh of embarrassment.

I had never cheated on anyone and certainly hadn't knowingly hurt anyone. I thought of myself as a nice, reliable, honest person who could, at times, be quite naive.

I could see that Billy, who was walking a few steps in front of me, was arguing with his mother but I knew he was also listening to my conversation with his father. Billy turned and looked at me after I had answered his father's questions. I smiled at him, expecting a smile in return, but instead I received a frown. He instantly turned around and continued rowing with his mother. His father and I continued to walk in silence, but he seemed content with my responses. As we neared our town we parted company with his parents, who were a little worse for drink, said goodnight and made our way home to 202. Billy seemed a little quiet for the rest of the journey. Putting my arm through his as

I normally did, I asked if he and his mum were okay after their disagreement. My inquiry was ignored as he marched quickly down the hill even though I was struggling to keep up with him. After repeated requests for him to slow down, he held my arm tight in his and almost dragged me home. I was thankful to arrive safely at our destination, where his brother and Samantha, Dave's girlfriend, were babysitting. They liked the privacy once Anna had gone to bed and they immediately assured me how well behaved she had been. Noticing Billy was in a strange mood, they made their way to the door to leave. Looking concerned, Dave asked,

'Are you okay? Billy looks a little quiet have you had a row?'

'No, not us, he and your mam had words but I don't know what it was about; I was talking to your dad most of the way.'

'Oh that's normal for that pair when they've had a drink. As long as you're OK.' He smiled and left.

I didn't think any more of Billy's disagreement with his mother and put the kettle on to boil in order to make a cup of tea. While it boiled, I nipped up to check on Anna. All was well; she slept contentedly. Kissing her lightly, I pulled up the blankets, tucking them in around her just like my mum used to do for me, which would always make me feel safe. I shut her door quietly, leaving her to her dreams. I made my way downstairs and looked at Billy as I walked through the living room heading for the kitchen. I noticed he looked very solemn and his head was slightly bent forward as if avoiding eye-contact with me.

'Are you okay, Billy?' I asked while handing him a cup of tea. 'You're not your usual self tonight,' thinking maybe his words with his mum were a little more serious than a slight disagreement. He didn't reply. He seemed pensive, so I decided not to push it. We drank our tea and made our way up to bed. Still very quiet, he got into our small single bed and watched while I got undressed and moved near the bed. My usual smiley nature failed to lift his spirits. On my attempt to get into bed, he kept hold of the blankets tightly, holding them down and preventing me from entering the bed.

'Budge up?' I joked in a jolly manner but he didn't move making me struggle to get into bed.

He looked different: his expression looked serious and his skin a little pale, so I thought it better to just be quiet and go to sleep. I leaned over to kiss him goodnight, which encouraged his mood to change. He returned my kiss and even became a little amorous. As the kissing turned passionate, I suddenly felt myself flying through the air. Something had tightly gripped my throat. It was dark and in the glow of the street lamp I could see the shape of Billy standing before me.

'You fucking whore,' his tone was menacing, his face close to mine.

My head banged into the corner edge of the wardrobe, causing me to feel dizzy. It was hard to catch my breath as his hands tightened around my neck. Dazed and confused, I tried to focus on his face. That's when I saw the green eyes of a monster: even though it was subdued lighting from the street, these eyes were piercing and evil. I couldn't comprehend the words being yelled at me as my hands frantically grabbed at his trying to gasp for a breath of air. I managed to grip hold of one of the offending hands and manically pulled in order to remove it from my throat. I gasped a deep breath. I felt his hand return to its hold and squeeze even tighter. Kicking out, trying to feel the floor, I was suspended in mid-air, thrashing my limbs to gain escape. Panic set in. My face began to burn with the pressure building in my head and my eyes felt like they were bulging; the tears streaming down my cheeks began to sting as my eyes began watering profusely. My head began to pulsate as I got weaker and my struggle for life lessened. Suddenly one of his hands released its grip, which allowed me to take in a deep breath. This made me feel strange and giddy. I stopped struggling savouring the intake of breath and expecting the other hand would soon be released. I closed my eyes and turned away from his face, not wanting to see those monstrous eyes. A few seconds later I realised he had no intention of setting me free, so I turned back towards him in an attempt to reason with him. I opened my eyes just in time to see a clenched fist heading straight towards me. As his grip got tighter around my throat I couldn't move out of the way of the impending fist. Screaming wasn't an option - it wouldn't have made the slightest difference and the only purpose it would have served would be to scare Anna. I couldn't breathe. I felt my body go limp as my struggling ceased. The collision of his clenched fist landed on the left side of my face, impacting with my eye. I felt the thud as the back of my head smashed into the wardrobe's edge. I felt my head split and blood surge down my hair and drip onto my naked body. I wasn't sure which made me collapse; the facial punch, the crack of my skull, or just the pure shock of what was happening to me. A while later I found myself in a heap on the floor in front of the wardrobe. I don't know how long I had been unconscious. My initial thought was to get to safety, so I scurried across the floor on all fours and hid in the corner of the room, curling up into a ball. I began sobbing uncontrollably. I heard a sharp, deep voice snapping at me. I couldn't see Billy as my eyes were filled with a mixture of tears and blood, which blurred my vision. The pain in my head was keen, throbbing like my terrified heart.

'Stop being melodramatic.'

I couldn't speak. I was trembling in shock. He ordered me get into the bed; I didn't respond or look at him. I felt I was that little girl in the big Gothic house I grew up in; avoiding the monster down the long dark hallway, thinking that if I didn't look in the monster's eyes he couldn't get me. Billy jumped out of the bed and headed towards me. I flinched and felt I was going to vomit in fear. Terrified I was in for another beating, I curled up even tighter, using my arms to cover my stomach, my unborn baby. I couldn't bear to lose another child. I could see his feet standing before me, so I prepared myself for more violence, to my relief; he turned and walked away from me bellowing:

'I said get into fucking bed. I'll sleep downstairs.'

He stormed out of the room, slamming the door behind him. I stayed in the corner for a while expecting his return. Eventually satisfied he was downstairs, I attempted to stand, but the weakness and pain I was experiencing prevented me let so I crawled towards the bed on my hand and knees. I saw blood dripping from my face and hair, leaving a trail on the carpet. I crawled slowly and kept as quiet as possible so as to not infuriate him even further. On reaching the bed, I used its leg to carefully lift myself onto the mattress and frantically pulled blankets around me for a little comfort in my fear. I listened to hear if Anna had heard anything and had been awakened, thankfully she seemed to have slept through my ordeal. I stifled my cries, as sobbing took over, by stuffing a sheet into my mouth. My nose was badly bleeding my right eye was painful and almost closed with the swelling, my head oozing blood from the gash at the back. I curled around my unborn child and buried myself under the covers, knowing I daren't go to sleep in case I didn't wake up. I lay stemming the blood with the sheet, sobbing quietly into the pillow. What had just happened was beyond my comprehension. It was a very long and lonely night as my thoughts ran through all the warnings I had been given at the start of our relationship; my friend Beth's attitude when he was around - she couldn't wait to get away; Mark's request to be careful because of Billy's violence; the girl in the chip shop who advised mum to be 'worried'. What a fool I had been. Then came the self-blame; I must have done something to have deserved the beating. He had never been nasty to me before. Had it been the smile after I told his dad I was a good girl? Did he think I was smiling because I was lying? I went over and over it in my mind, but still I couldn't understand why he did this to me. I lay quiet through the night, afraid of a repeat performance. As dawn broke and daylight arrived, I began to think about my mum. I needed her. The thought of Anna waking up filled me with dread. I knew I couldn't hide in my bed forever. I had to try and wash my face before she saw me. I cautiously crept out of bed. As I stood up I began to feel faint, so I steadied myself and sat back down on the bed's edge. My thoughts turned to Billy. What mood would he be in when I came face-to-face with him? How should I react? What would his reaction be? It wasn't something I was looking forward to. I knew I had to finish this relationship, but how would I get him out of here? Maybe he had already left? Just then I heard him snoring and my hopes of never having to see him again were dashed; the sickening thought of having to face this monster filled me with terror. When the dizziness eased I slowly rose, but the pain in my head was unbearable. I heard a kind of dull buzzing in my ears and dried blood was blocking my nasal passage. With my throat sore and swelling, breathing became increasingly difficult. Trying to be careful, I quietly made my way across the floor hoping not to alert Billy I was awake. Reaching for my dressing gown on its hook at the back of the door, I nervously opened the door, all the time listening in case I could hear Billy downstairs. I could - thankfully he was still snoring. Creeping into the bathroom, staying aware he could appear at any moment to continue his vicious attack, I held on to the door as one foot nervously stepped onto the landing. The bathroom was just ahead of me - maybe one more step - but in my confused and frightened state it could have been a million miles away. Trembling, I grabbed the bathroom door handle and made my way into the room, closing the door as quietly as possible. Locking it to prevent any intrusion, I guided myself by touch around the wall towards the toilet. My eye was closed by the swelling and the pain in my head was making it difficult for me to see out of the other. I sat on the toilet sobbing. I felt wretched and vulnerable. I laid my hands on my protruding stomach in the hope of feeling my baby moving, terrified at the thought I might lose it. A slight movement assured me it was still alive and somehow gave me the strength to pull myself together for the sake of Anna. Using the sink to lift myself, I stood before the mirror. I steeled myself for what I was about to see. What I saw sent shockwaves through my body. Rigidly holding onto the sink for support, I forced myself to look: my left side of my face was swollen to double its size and covered with various shades of purple and black from rebounding into the wardrobe. Stained by dried blood, my blonde hair was matted and stuck to my cheek; my right eye seemed to be non-existent as the swelling buried it deep into its socket. I felt I was going to vomit. I gently touched the back of my head to feel a lump the size of a tennis ball covering the back. I could feel the hard blood which had run from the open gash caused by the collision with the wardrobe. My legs buckled beneath me as I took in the extent of his rage. Lowering myself onto the side of the bath, I sat in disbelief and shock. I turned on the tap, filled the sink with warm water and used a soft face flannel to try and clean my injuries the best I could. Washing my hair wasn't an option as I felt too light headed. Doing the best I could, I carefully cleansed the blood away, only to see the extent of the bruising which was still occurring. I heard Anna waking up and worried what Billy would do if she woke him, so made my way quietly towards her bedroom door. Opening it slightly enabled me to hide the horror of my face from her.

'Can you play in your room for a little while Anna? I will fetch you soon for breakfast - mummy has had an accident and needs to have a bath.'

She was quite happy to do as I asked. After a painful bath, I attempted to gently cover my bruises with foundation makeup. Walking into Anna's room was hard. I calmly said,

'Don't be afraid when you see me, Anna. I'm OK - it just looks bad.'

I entered her room; the look on her face was one of shock. Tears filled her eyes as she scanned my swollen face with her little wet blue eyes that sparkled in the light of the sun shining through her bedroom window. I have never forgotten her reaction.

'What happened, mummy?' She asked, moving towards me - putting her gentle arms around my waist to console me. I fought back the tears as I quietly said to her:

'I have fallen down the stairs sweetheart. I just look bad but I'm alright.'

It was the first of many lies.

Picking out her clothes for the day, I was thinking 'thank God it's the school holidays'. I felt so ashamed to have been beaten. With her clothes in one hand and her hand in the other, I took her into my room to dress her so she would stay with me while I attempted to dress myself. Every movement made me feel faint. My head was sore and pounding and I felt the pain was getting worse.

'Careful, mummy, don't fall again, go slow,' Anna begged as we ventured downstairs.

I led her straight into the kitchen, placing my finger on her mouth to keep her quiet as we passed the sleeping monster on the settee. Anna was watching me closely; if I cried then she would cry she stayed strong because I did. I had to be strong, for her sake. I started to make tea quietly, but Billy must have heard me and shouted sternly,

'Two sugars.' It was an order, not a request.

Coldness ran through me. I tried not to react for fear of frightening Anna. As if nothing had happened, I took in his tea. He lit a cigarette and took his tea in silence, ignoring the fact I was there as he stared out of the window. No words passed between us and I returned to Anna, who was tucking into her cereals. He appeared in the kitchen to pour himself more tea; his sudden appearance startled me. I jumped with nerves as my stomach turned somersaults. Billy laughed.

I had no other choice but to leave as soon as he went out to the pub, but in the meantime I had to carry on as normal, pretending the same as he did, like nothing had happened.

It was a hot morning and the heat was adding to my discomfort. I sat outside on the doorstep of the kitchen watching Anna play and feeling very sorry for myself. The atmosphere was strained, as neither of us spoke about the previous night's ordeal. I could smell his cologne, so I knew it wouldn't be long until he was off to the pub. He came towards the door, knowing that I had been deep in thought over the last hour. Moving to one side to enable him to pass me, his leg brushed my arm. I froze rigid at the feel of him. I physically fought off the need to vomit. A steeled coldness ran through my veins as I felt my body turning icy cold with dread. He stepped off the last of the two steps, his closeness causing me to tremble. As he prepared to walk up the path I heard the words, in his sharp menacing voice,

'Don't even think about it.' His tone was nasty and frightening.

I couldn't find the words to reply to the man I no longer recognised. I turned my head just far enough to see out of the open eye: his face was glaring at me. His expression was odious his top lip curled round inside his mouth, showing his tobacco-stained teeth as he continued.

'You dare try to leave and I will find you,' he snarled as he glared at the terrified young woman before him. 'I will rip that baby out of your stomach. You think last night was bad?' His eyes were as green as the monsters in the night as he threatened, 'I'll kill you and your bastard kids.'

His words rang deep within me. I felt a terror growing from within my core within seconds it had engulfed me. With that parting statement, he walked up the path and slammed the gate. I heard the clattering of metal as the latch grabbed the catch, without looking back, he was gone. It was a sound that in the next two years was to cause both relief and terror.

I knew all hopes of leaving were gone. I sat on the doorstep trying to summon up the courage and strength to stand up and move. My body wouldn't work; I looked at my legs willing them to move. They wouldn't. All I could see was two limbs uncontrollably shaking. Eventually, after about an hour, I managed to stand. Holding on to the door and using the walls, I made my way into the kitchen where I sat dazed for most of the day. I thought how stupid I had been: my thoughts turned to all the warnings that I had been given by friends and family and how stupidly I had ignored them. I worried for my unborn baby. The threat he made was not an idle one, after what I had received the night before I knew was he capable of carrying it out. The look in his eyes was pure hatred, pure evil. I could leave now and hope he wouldn't find me, but where would I go? I hadn't seen my family for weeks. How could I go and say you were right; how could I go back and ask for help after all their warnings? If he could beat me whilst I was carrying his child, he could do anything. What about my family? He could hurt or injure them and it would be my fault. I couldn't cause them harm. Billy was a dangerous man and if I left I knew he wouldn't stop until I was dead.

'Oh God, help me, please,' I begged. I was alone in my misery; I felt I had no-one to turn to.

As the hours passed, I returned back to the steps to keep an eye on Anna while she played. I must have fallen asleep with my head on my knees, as I was woken by Shirley, our next door neighbour.

'Are you alright, my dear?'

Her voice was gentle and in the background I could hear Anna giggling while playing with her toys. I felt Shirley's hand on my shoulder, gently shaking it to wake me. It startled me and again I jumped. As I started to become coherent, I heard her say,

'Anna said you had a bad fall on the stairs, are you sure you're alright?' She was a kind old lady in her 80s; she kept herself to herself, but occasionally I would pick up shopping for her and we would meet in our adjacent gardens for a chat, especially in summertime when Anna was out playing. Shirley would come out for a few hours to watch her she had a son and grandchildren but it was rare for them to visit.

'Sorry,' I said as I came out of my sleep. 'Yes I did apart from my face I'm fine.'

'You don't look it, my dear. Come in for a cup of tea, the kettles on.'

Her invitation was welcome and I would have liked to have accepted, but I declined the offer. If anyone was nice to me at that moment I think I would have told them everything and for her safety I didn't dare. I knew if Billy came back and I was in her house, he would have assumed I had told her the truth about my injuries. I feared another beating, and I had my children to think about. She could see I was afraid of something; her smile was gentle and empathetic as she said,

'Well, if you won't come in I suppose you have your reasons. I will bring you one out you look dreadful, my dear. You ought to see a doctor; you could have damaged your baby.'

I thanked her for her kindness and she left me the tea and went to chat to Anna. Anna thought I had fallen, so I had nothing to worry about and he hadn't punched my stomach so it shouldn't physically affect the baby. But I was worried about the fact I was probably in shock.

It was 4pm when Billy arrived home. I saw him walking down the street towards the house. His stature caused me to jump up in fright and I shook like a scared rabbit caught in the headlights of a car. I grabbed Anna from the garden and rushed her in the house, sitting her at the kitchen table with her doll. I started to get a meal ready for her, thinking if I was busy, he would leave me alone. I heard the gate slam behind him. Shirley shut and locked her door. I realised then that she knew I hadn't injured myself falling on the stairs. I felt like the liar I was. I followed his steps until he walked through the door. Though I acted brave, inside I shook like a leaf in a force ten gale. His manner was friendly as he came towards me. Smelling of drink and cigarettes, he kissed me on the cheek like he used to before he moved in. I began to cry, all the emotions of fear and pain flooding out. He put his arms around me and held me.

'It will be alright,' he said very calmly.

I seemed to relax and the crying slowed. He let go of me and said for me to go and sit in the living room, he would make the dinner. I did as I was told. I was not about to argue with him. I could hear him chattering and laughing with Anna as the pots and pans clattered. Deep down I was waiting for him to turn nasty again, so I listened to every word said between the man and child. My trust in him had gone. Around half an hour later he came in with a dinner for me on a tray, followed by Anna with her tray in her little hands. Handing me the tray of chips, beans and egg, he turned to take Anna's dinner while she jumped on the settee. He then gently placed it on her lap. I dare not behave hurt or sulk; upsetting him terrified me.

Life started to return to normal within a few weeks as the swelling receded and the bruises began to heal. I stayed indoors until, with the aid of make-up, I couldn't see them anymore. The incident was put behind us and never spoke of. For the next few weeks he was very loving towards both Anna and I.

He didn't say sorry.

12.15am 21st September 1985.

The top bolt of the gate opened, which jolted me out of my thoughts of the past. For a moment panic ran through me as I sat as still as possible in the chair beside the window; I realised I couldn't hear the dogs barking, so it dawned on me it was dad returning after his night out. Within minutes I heard his footsteps on the stairs; though I knew it must be him there was a slight doubt in my mind as I imagined Billy's feet nearing my room. I heard the steps getting closer then stop outside my bedroom door. I inhaled and held it while my eyes fixed on the doorknob, hoping it wouldn't open. Time stood still as I stared into the darkness of the room. I heard the footsteps begin to walk towards the door of my old room, and I slowly exhaled in relief as dad entered the room of my youth.

'Had dad bolted the gate?' I panicked as my eyes strained

towards the gate. I wasn't brave enough to go down and check, so I knew the rest of the night I would sit in the dark awaiting Billy's return. Being at my parent's home did nothing to make me feel safe, for all their good intentions. I was the only one who knew what he was capable of. The night was quiet - something that was alien to me. Living on the edge in a state of panic for over two years had taken its toll mentally, though I wouldn't realise to what extent for another eighteen years. I remembered my childhood in this house; it wasn't perfect, but I was a happy child. I was a different person then to the one now cowering in the dark. I looked over to mum's bed: Lilly seemed so tiny placed in the centre, with pillows lining the edges to prevent her falling. I began to wonder if we would ever return to our home and see her happy in her own cot. I took one last look across the park and checked the gate was shut and then walked over to my baby, climbing onto the bed and trying not to interrupt her sleep. Listening to her breathing, soft and gentle, it consoled me. I lay still in the night until I could see day dawning and heard the sound of the morning chorus; exhausted, my mind continued to recollect.

Billy seemed to be very proud as my baby bump grew. He took me around to his aunts, uncles and cousins, introducing me. I believed he was genuinely happy that we were soon to have a beautiful baby. My visits to Dr Wright showed everything was developing well. He wasn't told of the violence because it didn't seem to affect the baby, so I thought no-one needed to know. I was closely monitored due to the risk of stillbirth reoccurring, but I felt sure this baby would be okay. I hadn't suffered the same symptoms as I had done with Thomas. It was a quiet Sunday afternoon when I was six months into my pregnancy, and Anna was, as usual, at her dad's. Billy had been out for his Sunday pint and had returned in a good mood. I could see he had enjoyed the dinner I had cooked for him. He was beginning to feel drowsy, so I left him nodding off to sleep on the settee and went to lie on the top of my bed to rest, as we had planned to go out that evening. I heard him answer the telephone when it rang at approximately at 2pm. Half asleep myself, I heard him slam down the receiver. The thud of his feet came stomping up the stairs, which unnerved me. My head turned to face the door as he barged through it and into the room. He came towards me so quick I didn't get chance to speak. He bent down, gripping the side of the bed with both hands, lifting it with such velocity it turned upside down, trapping me underneath. Dazed and shocked, I heard his voice yelling:

'The next time your fucking boyfriend calls, make sure I'm out.'

I couldn't reply as the bed weighed heavy on me as I lay under it, face down. I had landed with a bump and instantly had pain in my stomach. He stormed out of the room shouting:

'You're a fucking whore you don't deserve to have a baby; after all you killed your last one.' The door was slammed so hard that the vibrations shook the floorboards of the room. Dazed, I lay trying to understand what had happened. I heard him return downstairs, still shouting and swearing at the top of his voice. I struggled to get from underneath the bed, as the mattress and blankets were wrapped around me. I lay for a while trying to compose myself, letting my racing heart calm, after which I found the strength to wriggle from the restraint of the bed linen and weight of the old steel bed frame, leaving it upturned. Once free, the anger of what he had said enraged me.

'What the hell was that about?' I shouted after him as I made my way downstairs in pursuit of the crazy idiot. 'What the hell was that for? You bastard, you could have killed our baby'.'

'So?' His response made him sound disinterested in what he had just done.

'Killed my Thomas? You pig!' I screamed at him, as it sunk in what he had said.

Yelling at him took him by surprise. I wasn't the scared girl he battered two months previously. He tried to restrain me as I moved aggressively towards him, until I stopped ranting and raving at him. He held my arms taut to prevent my hitting him in my anger at the accusation of killing my son. Exhausted, I ended the verbal attack, not caring if he retaliated; instead he calmly explained that the phone rang and a man asked to speak to me.

'Did you ask who it was? It could have been anyone; a

salesman, my brothers, my dad, you idiot,' I screamed at him. I couldn't believe how I was attacking him for a change - in doing so, I didn't get punched.

'Sit down, you'll hurt the baby,' he grinned as he spoke. He found my outburst rather amusing.

'And you won't - by throwing bed on top of me?' I snapped back. Storming out of the door, I headed for the quiet of the seat in the garden. He later came out with a cup of tea when he saw I had calmed down, saying:

'How was I to know who it was?'

'Easy, you ask them,' I replied, taking the tea.

I felt like throwing it at him, but thought better of it; pushing it further would have been foolhardy. He returned inside the house and must have fallen asleep. I remained in the garden, hoping to be calmer before Anna returned home. My mind was wondering who could have called me on a Sunday, and for what? Time passed and Mark was at the gate with Anna. By this time I had bruises appearing all over my body. Unfortunately I didn't notice they were visible on my arms until Mark saw them and asked what had happened; I made some excuse, and hugged Anna as she said,

'Mummy keeps falling downstairs, don't you mummy? Daddy rang you earlier but you wouldn't speak to him.' She ran off indoors to the corner of the room, towards her toy box.

'Yes, I wasn't very well and wanted to ask if I could bring her home early. Billy put the phone down on me,' he explained, with a worried expression on his face. 'I hope I didn't cause you any trouble. Is everything alright?' He asked, noticing my subdued demeanour.

I said it was and he turned to leave, walking up the path to the gate. I watched as he opened and closed it behind him. He looked back at me as I stood at the bottom of the path, a worried look on his face. I forced a smile. Why hadn't I got the strength to tell him what was happening? I questioned myself as I watched him walk away. A lump appeared in my throat and, for a split second, self-pity began to creep into my thoughts, but just as quickly it disappeared.

I walked into the living room, leaving Anna playing with her toys and watched Billy as he snored in his drink-fuelled sleep. I remembered the man I met and how nice he could be, which made me wonder what I had done to make him hurt me so much. All I had done was be me, a warm, honest and loving young woman. I felt a little better having stood up to him; it seemed to make him back off. Anna came running in with an insect she had found and in her playful nature she had woken Billy. I watched him carefully to make sure he wasn't in a bad mood; he wasn't. He told her to bring the creature over to him and they had a good discussion about it.

'Tell Billy why daddy rang this afternoon, Anna,' I said, my eyes sternly fixed on Billy.

'Cos he poorly and wanted to bring me home,' she answered, unaware she was clearing up of some awful accusation.

Billy scowled at me. Not acknowledging what had been said, he continued to play with Anna's little insect.

He didn't say sorry. Billy never did.

Things were never right after that incident. Billy realised Mark was beginning to suspect his treatment towards me was getting violent and I was ordered to tell him that he was to pick Anna up at the gate from now on. I argued but it was futile arguing with a man like Billy. It didn't occur to me that he knew in the future there would be worse states for Mark to witness. It began to be every time Billy went for a drink, something would happen. Occasionally, I was made to go with him in the daytime, and it was easier to be with him than to cope with allegations of having men in the house while he was out. He obviously didn't trust me, or if he did it was a good way of invoking an argument, which led to violence - only it was me on the receiving end. If someone upset him, or his family interfered in his life, or someone didn't lend him money, it would always be my fault and a beating would occur. He was very controlling. I couldn't speak to anyone when I was out, even those I had known all my life. It was better not to speak than to incite his wrath. I found myself weakening and losing weight with the stress of the lectures and beatings. I dared not go out anywhere when he left the house. I always thought he was hiding somewhere, waiting to catch me and I dared not take the risk. He came home one Monday afternoon and had been in the pub all day instead of work; he had given up his job and was in an awful mood.

'We're going to a darts match tonight.'

'I'm not,' I snapped back.

'You are, so go and get ready.'

'What about Anna?'

'Mam's having her for the night she's not at school.' (It was October half term holidays). 'Our Maggie's popping down for her.'

'We haven't eaten yet, I'm hungry,' hoping he would reconsider. He didn't.

'Mam will feed Anna and I'll cook while you get ready.'

His sister and her boyfriend arrived to take Anna to their house, which she loved, and I didn't mind except for the fact I was never asked. I was told which annoyed me as he seemed to take control of everything, including my daughter. When Maggie had left, an argument flared up between us. It was getting out of hand and I feared his fists. For some reason and totally out of character, I started smashing up the living room. I threw ornaments at him: as he ducked, they smashed against the wall. The ashtrays were next, flying across the room full of his smelly cigarette ends, the ash peppering the carpet and curtains in a thin dusty film. Next were the chairs: wham, they hit the walls. I was a devil possessed. I couldn't stop. I was screaming and shouting out of control. The fear grew in me, but the more it did, the more I wrecked the room. I grabbed the telephone, ripping the cables out of the wall saying,

'There, no more fancy men ringing me.'

Finally, picking up the two-seater cottage suite settee, I held it aloft in my two hands. I was seven months pregnant. I looked in Billy's direction contemplating if I dared throw it at him.

'Why not throw it through the window?'

'Because I will have to pay for the damage,' I strained to say (the house was in my name so I was liable for any damage). His calmness made me worse. I threw it across the room; he stood very still watching and waiting till I had finished. With the furniture heaped up in the room, he calmly said,

'Have you finished?'

'Yes.'

I went upstairs to get myself ready, thinking "I'm not going to get out of this one". I returned to the living room to see he had straightened up the mess and reconnected the telephone by re-joining the wires. I sat down to a cup of tea waiting for me. As I sat down, he came in the room. I told him I couldn't face anything to eat. He ignored me. He went into the kitchen, returning with a tray which he placed it on my knees.

'EAT.'

'I'm not a dog,' I responded, though that's how he treated me.

I carried on drinking my tea as he came in and started to eat his dinner, looking across at me and seeing that I had no intention of eating what he had cooked. I couldn't. I felt ill after my physical outburst, which was out of fear and frustration rather than anger. I knew there would definitely be a beating that night if Anna was away. With her at home there might be a chance he wouldn't hit me in case of waking her up not that it ever did stop him, but there was always hope. The next thing I saw was his tray flying across the room; the plate hit my face. Full of hot food, it scalded me as beans burnt into my skin. The tray followed, its corner cutting my forehead; there were chips, beans and sausages all over me and the room. I was covered in food and blood as the cut bled profusely from my forehead.

There was a knock on the kitchen door; it was our lift to the pub for the darts night.

'Come in,' Billy said.

His friend Jim entered. He was a thick-set man with a shiny red face. I recognised him from the club; he was one of Billy's gambling mates. His eyes fixed on me as he saw the mess I was in. This was the first time anyone had walked in after an incident. I felt ashamed and embarrassed, knowing he would tell all who would listen in the club what a state I was in. I apologised for the mess, and went upstairs to change. I didn't rush - taking around thirty minutes due to having to wash my hair - I had no intention of hurrying. I could hear the two men chattering while they were waiting for me. As we were about to walk out of the door with Jim leading the way, Billy stopped - blocking the door with his body. He turned to me. He had that look in his eyes. I immediately lowered my head in an effort to avert his eyes.

'What are you apologising to him for?' His voice was menacing and he was so close I could feel his breath. I flinched.

'Because the house is a filthy mess,' I answered as I moved in intimidation.

'What's that have to do with him; you fucking him are you, behind my back?' His look said it all.

The terror inside began to rise from the pit of my stomach. I knew what was to come when we returned home that night. All I could hope for was he would have enough to drink that it would make him want to sleep, but with Anna away I knew there was little chance of being safe. I followed him up the path to the gate, keeping a few steps behind him so he couldn't reach me if he lashed out. I climbed into the back of the car. Billy got into the front passenger seat. I looked to the front of the car and caught a glimpse of Jim looking at me through the mirror. I could see the look of pity in his eyes as he scanned my face, seeing bruises fresh and fading as well as the large lump appearing on my newly cut forehead. I couldn't be bothered to look at him pitying me, so I sat quietly and looked out of the window for the whole of the thirty-minute journey. I didn't even join in any conversation or attempt to involve myself in chat. What was the point? I could be ignorant if I wanted to be; I was in for a beating anyway, so why should I be friendly and be accused of flirting? On reaching the pub I could hardly walk - my body had stiffened and was exuding pain. I walked inside to the crowd of dart players, but refused to look or speak to anyone. I had decided I wasn't going to pretend anymore. Everyone sees me bruised, bullied and frightened but no-one asks any questions. It seems they take for granted this was normal, it's just Billy. I watched the darts team enjoying themselves and I was hoping they would win or my life wouldn't be worth living. Suddenly I felt a numbness surrounding me; something inside my head was beginning to change. It sounds ridiculous, knowing that my life was hell and that it was about to get worse, but I relaxed. It was at that point I had come to terms with my life. I was trapped, but why worry? The worst he could do was to kill me. Maybe that would be for the best, because this wasn't a life. At least then my children would be free of him. I decided I wasn't going to fight him anymore I knew he got a kick out of seeing me struggle trying to fight him off, only now I had had enough. I knew the whole town knew what was happening to me, but no-one came to help. I felt I no longer existed in the human race, my life being taken by a bullying lout.

A few hours later we were dropped off at home; like a zombie I followed Billy into the house, hoping the beating wouldn't be too painful. I put the kettle on and with every movement he made I flinched, expecting a punch or a kick. He thought it was funny and taunted me all the more. Then suddenly he stopped ridiculing me - I couldn't hear him, which panicked me. This was a bad sign. I turned round, expecting to see him behind me. Fortunately he wasn't. I carefully walked to the door and cautiously looked in the living room. He had vanished. I sat quietly drinking my tea then I heard him snoring upstairs. I stayed downstairs for most of the night: getting into the bed with him was the last thing I wanted to do. After all, he had a habit of waking up sexually violent in the night. Starting to feel exhausted, I thought about my life. I knew it was getting too much to bear. After a few hours I went upstairs: Anna's bedroom door was open. I walked into her room. Her bed looked safe and inviting, so I lay dressed under her blankets. Before drifting into sleep I thought "he can't hurt me anymore, I'm numb to it".

How wrong I was.

Waking up in the morning, Billy realised I hadn't been in the bed. He appeared at Anna's open door. Seeing me under her blankets, he sneered menacingly saying:

'Don't think I've forgotten.'

I looked at him, knowing he meant he owed me a good hiding and that my expectation of when or where it would happen would entertain him all day. That evening he went out. I knew when he got home he would be in the mood to keep his word. I had put Anna to bed around 9pm. I didn't want her around when he got in from the pub. True to his word, without speaking, he walked in and grabbed me. With his hands around my throat, he lifted me out of the chair I was sitting on. With my hands on his arms,

I fought to pull him off. He stuck me against the living room wall. I saw his eyes turning green and the clenched fist heading straight to my face. I felt blood spurt from my lip and another blow collided with my eye. My hands stopped pulling at his. I felt weird. I must have blacked out. I came round to find him standing over me. I lay coughing, as blood was splattering out of my mouth. He left me when he saw I was conscious. I found it hard to get up off the floor, but managed to crawl into the kitchen, and using the legs of a chair, I managed crawl to my feet. The usual feelings of hurt and pain came, but I getting immune to it and didn't thrive on the feelings. I sat for hours with cold flannels or frozen food on my injuries. I endured the suffering and headaches quietly and alone as I knew no-one could help me.

The following Thursday was my appointed visit to the hospital for my thirty-week check-up. I had cancelled the earlier appointment due to bruises after a beating, giving them chance to heal before the staff at the hospital began to get suspicious. This visit was important as I was getting near the time I had lost Thomas. I couldn't believe my baby was surviving such violence; it seemed to be hanging on by sheer determination. I was thirty-two weeks when the appointment date arrived. I caught the bus and set off for my journey to the maternity centre in the city. Though it was a lonely journey and I had to catch two buses, it was the peace of being away from Billy I looked forward to. I remembered always wanting Mark to accompany me while I was pregnant with Anna and Thomas, but he never would; this time I needed to be on my own.

On my arrival, I made my way to the necessary department. I was nervous because I was still sporting bruises, especially around the face. I sat quietly and didn't interact with the group of excited expectant mothers. I couldn't find any enthusiasm for these appointments. After Thomas' stillbirth and the abuse I was experiencing at home, I dared not believe my baby was going to arrive safely. I had subconsciously hardened myself to the fact it was just a matter of time for it to slip away. I undressed very quickly in order to hide my thin and battered frame from the nurse. As I entered the examination room, I manoeuvred myself on the bed, carefully preventing any pain occurring from the bruises which would alert the nurse to my discomfort. I couldn't answer awkward questions. They monitored the baby's heartbeat and did the necessary tests and checks. To my relief, all was well. I felt weak after the examination, finding it uncomfortable walking to the bus stop at the end of the road. The pressure I was living under was beginning to take its toll. The bus shelter had two missing windows, so I perched on the edge to take the weight off the baby and my aching legs. Within a few minutes of waiting, a queue of people had appeared in the shelter. I began to feel claustrophobic and the noise of the traffic whizzing by my ears began to blend into one enormous buzzing inside my head. I felt I would pass out. I knew I must move from the busy road directly behind me; if I had fainted and fallen backwards into the road, I could have been killed or at worst survived and my baby killed. I stood up to move away from the shelter in the hope of self-protection. One slow step, then another, but on the third step I suddenly felt my face smashing onto the slanting gravel wall opposite the shelter just a few feet away. Unconscious, I slid down the wall, face first. I woke up in an ambulance that some kind person had rung for, even though it only had to drive a couple of hundred yards from the emergency entrance, around the island and back to the hospital doors. I heard a distant voice explaining to the paramedic what had happened. Within minutes I was being wheeled into the emergency unit. I felt weak and fragile. I worried I had fallen on my baby. My face felt extremely painful and wet.

'You're alright, my dear, you're in hospital.' The voice was blurred. 'No,' the voice insisted as I raised my arm to wipe the water on my face, 'don't touch your face; I'm afraid you have a nasty injury. I just want to check your baby is alright, so please try and keep still.' It was then I realised it wasn't water.

'What was the last thing you remember, Jeannette, can you tell me?' questioned a doctor.

'I felt faint and stood up,' was all I could tell them.

As they began to clean my face a nurse said,

'You may have a nasty scar under your eye. We cannot freeze it as it's too close to your eyeball, so I'm afraid it has to be stitched without anaesthetic. Your lip is very badly split, but we've cleaned it up and we need to stitch that too. Can we let anyone know you are here?'

I gave them our phone number and said his name was Billy. How I was to regret that. An hour went by as I lay on the trolley bed. I thought about my baby, about Thomas, then Anna. I thought how much I missed my family, I missed being loved and I needed them so much, especially mum. I couldn't even tell them I'm in hospital. I began to wonder how I could have been such a bad daughter and sister to be all alone in this world. In my confused and lonely state, my thoughts caused tears to trickle down my face, and the salt began to sting as they met the cuts in my face. I knew what being alone really meant now. Surely I didn't deserve the treatment I received at the hands of Billy? I made the decision that, no matter what Billy said or did, I was going to see my mum. My friends had all deserted me, knowing that if they visited it would cause me trouble with Billy. I saw only the people in the pub, and they felt sorry for me. I didn't want pity. I needed help. I wondered why no-one cared. They couldn't all be terrified of Billy. I was beginning to dislike the girl I was becoming. I composed my demeanour just as a nurse came past.

'Don't worry, dear, it will heal,' she said, as she patted my hand thinking I was upset at my accident. If only she knew, if only anyone knew the truth.

At that moment Billy appeared, all of a flutter probably scared I'd told them how he had been beating me. He stood over me, showing his false concern.

'She will be back soon we will look after her,' a nurse said as they wheeled me into theatre to stitch my face together. As I went through the doors my thought was,

'What's the point he will only rip it open again when he's drunk'.

The doctor working on patching me up was concerned that I never flinched as the needles did their work and didn't even seem upset about my ordeal. He asked me if I was alright, other than the injury; I knew in my mind what he was getting at. I suppose they see people in my state all the time, but I refused to answer him. I knew he had seen the sadness within me. As they pushed me into the recovery room, I saw Billy's face; mine was covered in blood and bruises from the stitching of my cuts. Billy's remark made my heart sink even further when he said,

'They can't blame me for this one.' Then he grinned. I knew then I didn't matter and neither did our baby.

On my arrival home, Dave bought Anna down after picking her up from school; she ran towards me, throwing her arms around me, saying,

'Poor mummy's had another accident.'

This time it wasn't a lie. Billy asked Dave to babysit that night. Shocked, I looked at him and said,

'I can't go out like this I feel too ill.' His stern look said that I would.

I did as he ordered and got ready and we left. Billy couldn't wait for people's reaction when they saw my faced cut and messed up. I couldn't put make-up on and I was very weak and unsteady on my feet. He got hold of my arm and pulled me up the road. He marched me from pub to pub, each full of eyes staring at me, looking at the cuts and bruises. I couldn't look at anyone, my eyes permanently lowered to the floor. I was getting weaker, but was too scared to say I needed to go home. I stuck it till closing time. The echo of Billy bragging that he didn't do it and that I had had an accident was rebounding around my tired, painful head. Eventually, after the parade, we finally headed for home. I was thankful the evening was over and felt on the edge of collapsing by time we arrived. I wouldn't have cared if I had died at that point, a feeling I would get used to. For that one night he gave me peace, for which I was grateful. A few weeks later, when I felt much stronger, I decided to go up to the town to do a little shopping. Since the accident Billy had let up on the violence, although the mind games and continual verbal abuse remained. He even allowed me out alone. Although visits to my parents and friends were not allowed, to go in a shop and maybe see someone I knew was nice. I was still sporting faint bruises where I had been stitched, but at least if anyone asked I didn't have to lie; the truth was easier to explain. I walked with Anna into the supermarket. I hadn't much money: since Billy had left his job and signed on the dole, the little money the government gave us was in his name, so he boozed or gambled it away. The maintenance cheque from the courts from Mark for Anna's care had come, so I had to buy food before Billy got hold of it. Anna and I had a steady walk up to the supermarket in town which was a mile and half away. It was nice to be out with Anna; we chatted and she held my hand all the way. She promised to take care of me after my accident. Happily we shopped around the aisles adding up the prices as I gathered groceries - as I only had £7.20. The shopkeeper down the road who changed the cheque for me let me off the usual 50 pence charge for cashing cheques. I think he had begun to feel sorry for me, as he was always seeing the various shades of bruising after benefit day. I appreciated it. I reached the end of one aisle, holding Anna's hand I turned to go down the next. I saw two people I recognised, though I hadn't seen them for a while: my parents. Mum was busy shopping - dad saw Anna run towards them excitedly. I slowly walked up the aisle behind her. Forcing a smile I fought back tears, pleased I watched Anna's delight. After hugging their granddaughter, their attentions turned to me.

'Hello, how are you?'

I couldn't think how to answer mum.

'Alright,' I shrugged my shoulders - lost for words.

My eyes were begging for help but they couldn't see it. My gaunt, pale face and skinny body (other than my baby bump) was painfully thin. Dad looked away - I saw the hurt in his eyes. Mum half smiled - like me - fought her tears. Not knowing what to do the left and continued shopping. That confirmed I was alone in this world. I continued to shop and walked back to 202, my excitement of being out-and-about quashed. I knew my parents would have protected me if I had asked for help but I couldn't. I was afraid. I feared Billy would hurt them too.

We got home rather late one evening after Billy's insistence that we go to one of his old work friends' birthday party. I had my misgivings as you would expect; nights out were never enjoyable for me and as I was getting well into my pregnancy I didn't want to be handling Billy's sadistic jealousy and drink-fuelled temper. Fortunately a lot of people I had known whilst growing up were there and it was nice to see friendly faces after being so isolated from life. Having women to talk to of my own age group was something that rarely happened and - as they were aware of Billy's character - they made an extra effort to include me in their conversations, though I admit I was pretty quiet compared to the girl they once knew. Within his gang of old work friends were a few men that had known me as a child, so they kept Billy engaged in conversation and chats away from the women, giving me chance to speak up about anything that was happening. The thing is I couldn't tell anyone what was happening even though I knew they would believe me. What could they do? Any interference would only serve to add to my misery. I felt trapped and had done since the first beating. Anna was at home with Billy's younger brother Paul, so I couldn't take the chance of opening up to anyone. Even so, though my words were guarded, I did enjoy a little freedom with people away from Billy's constant surveillance. Just for a few moments it was nice to relax and listen to general gossip. On the way home I realised Billy was going to question me, afraid of what I had told anyone. On arrival home, everywhere was quiet and Anna and Paul had gone to bed, so I popped up to check on them. Billy had followed me upstairs, having locked up for the night. I felt him watching me so I kept quiet, still wondering when the inquisition would start. I put on my nightdress and climbed into bed. Nervously I settled down to go to sleep, hoping his quietness would continue. I closed my eyes and started to drift off into sleep. Suddenly I felt his hands on me. With force he grabbed my arms so I couldn't move - he spun me around so quick I couldn't focus on what was happening. Shouting at him to get off me and to leave me alone, I tried to make him realise he would hurt the baby. My plea was ignored. My head was quickly smashed down hard onto the pillow. I was finding it difficult to breathe because my face was forcibly held into the pillow. I felt him clawing at my nightdress like an animal. I was frantically trying to wriggle free, trying to kick out, but my struggling did nothing except to excite him more. My cries and attempts to make him realise what he was doing were useless as his viciousness continued. Moving my head sideways as his grip loosened, I screamed for him to stop, repeating the words,

'No, Billy, get off me. No, stop it, the baby.'

Unable to move under his weight, I felt him push my pregnant tummy into the bed. I felt his legs pushing mine apart: I was still wriggling from side to side in an effort to prevent what he was about to do. I kicked out, hitting his leg with my heel, and infuriating him. He swore as he punched my head. Rather than stopping him, it intensified his brutality. I continued to cry and scream for him to stop, but was unheard in his drunken fury. Using my hair to jolt my head backwards, he dragged a pillow from beneath me. I felt my neck wrench, causing me to scream in pain. He placed the pillow over my head, securing it with his arm to smother my screams. He took my breath as he entered my body. He began raping me and there was nothing I could do to stop him. The pain was unbearable. Screaming in agony as he continued his animalistic attack, I heard a voice. Still painfully hard inside me he stopped. Sobbing uncontrollably, I felt his body lying on mine forcefully, squashing the breath out of me. I was unable to move. The voice was Paul's: he was shouting from behind the door for him to leave me alone. I lay quietly sobbing, hoping this would end my torment. It didn't.

'Get back in bed. Now,' Billy demanded. His voice was raging at the disturbance of his pleasure. I knew the kids had heard me screaming with the excruciating pain he was inflicting on me. He turned on the radio, which was at the side of the bed. The volume was turned full blast, drowning out my cries. I knew my ordeal wasn't yet over. I took the opportunity to try and reason with him, but again the pillow was tightly held over my head as my tummy was painfully flattened into the mattress. I was a helpless victim of his evil intent as he continued his violent attack. I tried to be brave and take the brutal assault. I closed my eyes and tried to close my mind to what was happening. I didn't want to frighten Anna any more than I already had. I held my breath while being pinned down to the bed. He got more and more excited knowing he had total control over me. The ordeal seemed endless. His thrust got more vicious as he grunted like the pig he was. My hands clenched the pillows; my cries were silent as he continued enjoying himself. When he had finished, he got off me. I lay still, trying to control my trembling body and trying to be quiet. The pain, the blood, the mess, was unbearable. He stood up at the side of the bed and put on his jeans. He stood over me watching as I cowered under the blankets, too scared to look in the monster's eyes.

'I hope you get AIDS, you fucking whore.' I listened to his footsteps as he made his way downstairs. I turned down the noise of the radio, leaving it slightly on to hide the sound of my sobbing. He had viciously raped me: the shame and humiliation was too much to bear. The sickness I felt was indescribable as I began to retch. I was in deep shock, causing uncontrollable shaking to take control of me. I gasped for air but couldn't breathe. There seemed to be no air in the room as my body changed from raging-hot and clammy, to ice-cold and dithering. I thought I was going to suffocate. I heard a faint knock on the bedroom door. I turned off the radio and tried to compose myself: it was Paul, who sounded frightened.

'Are you alright?' He asked. He was barely sixteen years old. 'Shall I fetch someone?' He obviously realised the situation was serious and I had been severely hurt.

'I'll be okay,' I stammered through my panic and sobbing. 'Please,' I begged him, 'go and look after Anna for me.'

'I hate him,' I heard him say as he returned to Anna. I listened to hear if I could hear her. I heard Paul comfort her saying,

'Your mum's okay. Shush go to sleep.'

My sobbing continued for hours; some for the horrific pain I was feeling inside my body, some for the fear I would lose my baby, and some for frightening the kids, for which I felt deeply sorry.

'Father in heaven, please help me, please free me from this life I am suffering. Please Lord, save my baby, forgive my stupidity in my young life,' I prayed over and over. Telling anyone what he had just done to me was going to be impossible because of the shame I felt. AIDS was the new disease of the 80s and everyone was confused and scared of it; being naïve, his wish for me to contract the disease haunted me for years until more was learnt about the virus.

From then on it was a regular thing, the rapes: it was unbearably degrading. Usually it preceded or followed a beating. I soon learnt to switch off from pain. I couldn't afford to let my children hear their mummy scream. After the ordeals, which were never just taking sex, I would deal with the damage to my body, but I was unaware of the mental damage this physical, sexual torture would cause in later life.

Day dawned and everyone was sleeping. I thought about my parents, my brothers, my friends, who were all gone. The stinging in my genital area was bad. I was ripped and bleeding. The pains in my stomach were, to my relief, subsiding. I needed to get in a warm bath, but I feared waking Billy. I lay there till the morning. I heard him come upstairs around 7am and, like a frightened little mouse, I hid under the blankets, my heart thumping, my mouth dry and my body trembling. Panicking, I tried putting a hand across my mouth to quell the uncontrollable cries of fear. I heard the flush of the toilet. Lying rigid with my eyes transfixed on the door, thankfully I heard him go back downstairs. Calming myself, I lay listening to every noise my abuser made in the room below me.

I waited until 7.30am, when I climbed carefully off the bed. I couldn't feel my legs beneath me as I staggered, using the walls of the room for support, until I reached the door. Trying not to collapse, I managed to get in to the bathroom, quietly locking the door and placing a linen basket against the door, to stop him attacking me further. Even though I knew it wouldn't make any difference, in my mind I thought I was protecting myself. I took off what was left of my nightdress and slowly climbed in a bath of tepid water to which I had added an antiseptic. The water stung. Lying in the warm bath, water covering my torn and battered body, I thought about ending it all by drowning myself. My head slipped under the water, but I did not dare breathe in. My mind was in turmoil as I realised I would be murdering my baby, it had held on, surviving against all the odds. Who was I to take its life along with mine, and Anna, what about Anna? Yes, she had her daddy; the poor child didn't deserve the mess I had bought into her life. I decided I must cope a little longer, maybe when the baby was born he would stop hitting me. I wasn't what he called me; I was not a whore, a cheat or a liar. In my confused and battered mind, I seriously believed he would be okay when the baby arrived. I washed myself carefully; it was hard to do being eight and a half months pregnant and cringing in pain at the slightest touch. I started to get upset thinking about my past, and the memories of Thomas came flooding back. I had a few days to go to the dreaded time of his death inside me, how could I think of suicide?

It was around that time the hatred for my-self began. I suppose I should have hated Billy, but somehow I had transferred the feeling onto myself, believing I was the cause of his atrocious behaviour. However I tried to put things right between us, his temper continued to get more and more vicious. I had fallen into his trap after he had duped me into thinking I had met a sweet caring man who loved me. It was beginning to dawn on me it wasn't children he wanted it was a child to tie me to him. Through his vile ferocious beatings and threats to my life, he knew I would be too terrified to leave him. He was right.

Once I had bathed and eased the immediate soreness of my body, I slowly made my way downstairs. Expecting him to be awake, I prepared myself for his glare of control, but I was relieved to see him asleep snoring loudly on the settee. Instead of feeling fear on seeing him, I felt nothing. I thought nothing I wanted nothing, except peace. On entering the kitchen, I saw Paul and Anna sitting quietly at the kitchen table, their eyes watching mine as I walked painfully slow into the room. The pity on Paul's face was evident as he tried to hide the tears in his pale grey eyes. I glanced at Anna - she unconvincingly ate her breakfast and pretended she had heard nothing of the night's events. I swallowed deeply, trying not to cry, for I knew it would cause both children to break down. I was completely demoralised: I knew there was no chance of escape.

After my parents had spoken to me in the supermarket - mum decided to contact me, even though it was only to tell me about my grandparents' golden wedding anniversary. It was excuse enough to enable me to go and see them. I didn't tell Billy where I was going. I knew he would be out in the pub for hours, so

I dressed myself the best I could and made the effort to look as normal as possible. A long-sleeved cardigan over my flared maternity dress usually hid the cuts and bruises; it also disguised how thin I had become over the last four months. Foundation make-up was magical at covering bruises on the face and neck. I knew Anna was missing her grandparents and would be happy to see them, so we slowly set off on our journey. I impressed on Anna we could only visit her grandparents for a short while and on the condition she didn't tell them of anything that had happened to me.

'I promise, mummy,' she answered in the excitement of her outing.

As I reached the park opposite my parents' house, I suddenly felt very daunted by the prospect of disguising my dismal life from them. They were the people who knew me more than anyone else, maybe deep down I was hoping they would see my tormented soul in my eyes and refuse to allow me home. Nerves were getting the better of me and if I hadn't had Anna with me I would certainly have turned around and returned to 202. I was strong enough to take the punishments off Billy, even the rapes, but under no circumstances was I strong enough to talk about what he was doing to me. Billy had embedded fear deep within me and I knew I was taking a chance visiting my parents. Hiding my life had become an art and I had become good at it. As we reached the gate, I took a deep breath and pushed it open. Anna ran into the kitchen, making an excited entrance. I could hear the fuss being made of her and deep down wished my appearance would excite the same pleasure. I walked in the door and was shocked to see mum had gone completely grey-haired and was now wearing glasses. I felt like I hadn't seen her for years. She looked at me and, without a word, put her arms around me and held me: we both cried. Dad sat cuddling Anna, his strong demeanour cracking with the sight of his beautiful granddaughter.

'I'm not going to ask you if you're alright, I know you're not.'

I didn't answer mum. We talked about everything the family had been doing, how everyone was. She told me about my new niece and nephew, and that my brothers said I had been to post them a congratulations card when their children were born. I explained that when they saw me in the supermarket I had had an accident and told them the details, although I got the impression they didn't believe me, so I didn't push it. In general we had a good visit. Before I left mum, hugged me again asking,

'Shall we see you at your aunts for grandma's celebrations?'

'Nothing or no-one would stop me from being there, mum, other than giving birth,' I replied and we both laughed.

'You know where we are if you need us,' she said, as Anna and I walked through the gate. I needed to get back before Billy returned home. I talked to Anna on the way home, explaining why we mustn't tell Billy we had been to see them. She promised she wouldn't tell. She didn't.

4.40am September 21ˢᵗ.

Lilly was still sleeping soundly. I rose from where I had been lying next to her while deep in thought. I felt very cold on this bright autumn morning, but as I put on a cardigan belonging to mum I knew I wasn't doing this because I was cold. Hugging it close, I wrapped myself in the old woollen garment to feel the warmness of mum. I made my way to the window and stared into the nothingness of the sky which hadn't yet burst into daylight, but was slowly leaving the darkness: it had a strange resemblance to my life. I heard the muffled noises of Lilly stirring I turned to look at her, but once again she slipped back into sleep. I half smiled to myself as it dawned on me I had left the horror of 202 and had my daughter safe with me. I sat in the chair under the window as my eyes began to feel the heaviness of sleeplessness. Letting them gently close, my mind drifted to the day my little miracle arrived.

Little Miracle

The day before my grandma's golden wedding festivities, the promise I had made to mum had to be broken. Knowing I would be the only grandchild not attending, I eased my disappointment knowing in my stead would be their eldest great-grandchild, my Anna. I was eight days before my due date. I had begun to bleed and pain shot through my abdomen. I had flashbacks to my previous pregnancy I had to get myself to hospital urgently.

'Oh no, not again, hang on baby, we've come this far, you're strong, you must be to have survived this far, please, please hang on,' I begged as I found my ante-natal card and got to the telephone.

I instinctively calmed myself and shut my mind off from the pain. I rang for the ambulance; I explained my symptoms and they immediately put the doctors on alert that I was coming in. Next, I made the phone call to my parents who had been put on standby. I wanted Anna to stay with them so I wouldn't have to worry about her alone with Billy during this anxious time. Her daddy was at work as it was a Friday and depending on the outcome of the next few hours there could be a chance I wouldn't be returning to 202. I packed Anna's clothes for a lengthy stay and found her a pretty dress for the anniversary party. I sat quietly and as calm as possible under the circumstances. I feared the rape a few days earlier had damaged my unborn child, as I hadn't felt it move since the attack. I waited for both to arrive. Dad came first; with Billy out at the pub I had no worries with dad coming to the house.

The last time he was at my house was a scary ordeal, thanks to Billy's evil torment. Dad and mum had taken Anna out with them for the day to visit friends in Yorkshire. I was five months pregnant at the time - just two weeks after the first violent episode - and was still a little afraid of Billy. For some reason I expected them to return around 6pm, but when they hadn't returned by 9pm I was worried and quite fraught, thinking they had had an accident on the roads. Billy saw an opportunity to enjoy himself: he started his torment by telling me they were wrong to do this, they should have rung when they knew that they were going to be late. He started to call my parents dreadful, derogatory names. I really didn't need to listen to this while I was worrying if they were all alright. He must have seen the stress appearing in my face, as he suddenly shut up calling them and stood to leave the room. He returned and sat on the settee, very quietly staring at me: I had the feeling he was going to do something. To my horror, I saw a hammer in his hand. My instant thought was I was going to be beaten with it. I started to feel my body going into a slight tremble. Trying to hide the fear in my voice, I asked,

'Why have you got that?'

Toying with it in his hands, while grinning with his sickening thoughts, he replied,

'When the bastard brings her back, he's going to get this smacked into the side of his head as he walks in the door. Kill him outright in one blow, good - hey? The bitch as well if she dares to come in.' I saw total hatred in those green monstrous eyes. Terror took hold of me and I began to shake uncontrollably. Frightened for my parents' lives, I had to pick my words carefully to try to convince him they haven't done anything wrong and I was just worrying for no reason, 'just being stupid'. This was all part of his game, to see how scared he could make me. He continued to play with the hammer, his hand on the shaft and making a pretend thump with it in front of me. When I begged him not to, he stood up and walked over to me, putting the hammer to the side of my head where he gave me a choice, dad or me? I froze as I felt the cold hard steel on my skin. I couldn't find the words to say. Billy laughed, taunted and mimicked me. I knew he was crazy enough to hurt dad. He turned away from me and walked into the kitchen taking the tool with him, placing it head down on the floor next to the door, ready for dad's appearance. Visions of dad dead with his head bashed in and blood everywhere were flashing in front of my eyes as I felt panic setting in. Following Billy into the kitchen, I saw him turn away from the menacing tool. Suddenly I felt myself making a grab for it. I didn't know what I would do with it when I had it; my thinking hadn't gone that far in my erratic thought-process. Billy saw me and made a grab for my arm preventing my reach, so I kicked it towards the door and pulled it as hard as I could out of his grasp. I made a dive onto the ground, falling into the closed door. Almost immediately Billy landed on top of me in his desperation to take the offending hammer from me. I refused to let it go hanging on to it while he dragged me from one side of the kitchen to the other. My refusal to let go of it was a cause of amusement to him, as he dragged me up to my feet by means of the hammer. I refused to cry in pain as I fought to keep the instrument that could render my parents dead. Realising he would have to kill me first, he gave up the struggle, but not before he pushed me so hard that I flew into the wall still clutching the hammer. In my dazed state I lay bent double, holding the hammer close to me. I wished I had had the nerve to use it and finish this vile bully once and for all. I hadn't the guts. I stayed in position until I regained a clearer head, feeling sick with exhaustion. I opened the kitchen door. A fresh breeze of air hit me through the gap in the door and I inhaled a deep breath that caused light-headedness, but I knew I must hide the hammer. Carefully negotiating the two stone steps, I managed to walk with the aid of the wall around the back of the house. Looking towards the kitchen window, I checked Billy wasn't watching me then shoved the tool into the hedge at the top of the neighbouring house. I began to feel sick. I didn't know if it was the strain of the struggle, the collision with the wall, relief he wasn't about to kill dad, or the thought that I wanted to kill him. As I returned into the daunting house of horror, I saw Billy in the living room. He glared at me as he walked through the stairs door and thumped his way upstairs to be away from me.

'If they ever come up here again I swear I'll kill them,'

The sound of each car outside on the road filled me with anxiety. My heart sank as each one passed by, but also brought a sense of relief, as I feared Billy's vindictiveness as soon as they arrived. Because of how he had behaved earlier, I knew he was spoiling for confrontation and I knew once Anna was safely back and in bed, I would be his target to vent his frustration. I realised my arms were turning blue from the earlier struggle. My body was beginning to stiffening so I slipped on a cardigan to cover the reddening of bruises. At last my dad's car pulled up outside our gate; mixed feelings took over me as I tried to control the feelings of relief and expectation. Meeting them at the door, the tears uncontrollably erupted.

'What on earth are you crying for? You weren't worrying about her, were you? You know she is safe with us, you silly girl. Here she is.' He gave Anna a kiss and returned to his car having said goodnight. He was a little disconcerted, thinking I didn't trust him. If only he had known the real reason for my outburst.

77

Soon after dad had collected Anna, the ambulance arrived. Picking up an overnight bag I walked out of the door, conscious that if Billy saw me he would insist on accompanying me and that was the last thing I wanted. I had decided that if I lost my baby I would tell the doctor everything about Billy's violence towards me, whatever the consequences. Being in a safe environment I felt ready to ask for help, knowing they would call the police; with no-one else involved, I knew this would be my only chance.

'Are you all alone?'

I quickly climbed into the vehicle, praying they would quickly close the door.

'You don't look in labour to me,' he quipped.

Still I didn't reply, waiting for them to get a move on.

'You will be back later.'

'No I won't.' I finally acknowledged the man trying to lighten the situation. 'Not without my baby being born.' I went on to explain my troubled childbirth history which caused his attitude to change to a more serious tone. I really wasn't in the mood to make light conversation and at that point he realised. He wrote notes and called the hospital with an estimated time of arrival. I sat quietly, trying to keep my thoughts positive in my solemn and lonely world.

Billy always threatened that he would kill me if anything happened to his baby - even though I had become his punch-bag since I was four-and-a-half months pregnant and even more so - since my accident outside of the hospital. He tormented me with his vicious allegations of murdering my own son, Thomas. If this baby didn't survive it was me to blame - not his sadistic violence. On arrival at the ante-natal ward, I was wheeled into a private room. I undressed and put on the crisp white cotton gown while the nurse asked a barrage of questions. When they asked me about the bruises up and down my body, I convinced them that I was clumsy: the nurse gave me a look of disbelief. When I was weighed, their thoughts were confirmed. I had lost over half a stone in weight since my last check-up two-weeks previous. I knew they weren't stupid but as the tests came back normal, they didn't query me any longer. Another nurse came into the room with a heartbeat monitor and attached the electrodes to my baby's head to keep an eye on the heartbeat and to measure the strength of contractions. To my horror there was no output, a heartbeat wasn't heard.

'No not again, please not again,' I pitifully cried.

'Don't worry, my dear,' said the nurse, as she frantically searched in vain. I stared at the latest technology in despair, praying for a beep or a fluctuation in the single flat line showing on the monitor screen. I can't explain to you the feeling of dread that consumed me at that point. In tears the nurse fled from the room, but soon reappeared with a senior nurse.

'Now then, now then', she repeated 'you know sometime these machines play up. Please keep calm my dear.' She portrayed a woman in control, but sadness in her voice was hard to disguise. She wiggled the wires attached inside me but to no avail. She removed them. A look of determination appeared in her eyes - she forced a smile that didn't convince me - she pushed the monitor out of the room, followed by the other nurse that was supposed to be caring for me. I lay on the bed in a state of doom. I thought nothing, because I dare not face what might have happened. A few minutes later a doctor appeared, followed by a new monitor being pushed by both nurses. As they plugged the monitor into the plug socket, the male doctor commenced to use the old-fashioned heartbeat funnel in shape of a small trumpet. A look of relief spread over his face and then turned to a smile.

'Your baby is fine, Jeannette - the monitor wasn't working properly.'

Immediately, my baby was hooked up to the monitor and a loud muffled heartbeat was beating strong and clear. Everyone in the room had tears of joy in their eyes including me. The doctor apologised for the frightening experience and promised they would do all they could to prevent a reoccurrence of the past delivery. After the initial reading told them I wasn't actually in contractions, they decided to keep me in under supervision. As soon as I was alone in the room, I held my breath and pushed from inside. This gave a reading of contractions occurring, though only slight. I soon realised if I controlled the pattern of the highs on the line, it would read it as my baby was trying to be born. Dangerous or not, I needed my baby out, alive. After five hours the reading was enough to cause them concern: after all, my last baby died at this exact week and my first child Anna was stuck and, being three weeks late, she almost died too. So after consultation, to my relief they agreed it would be safer to have the baby here instead of leaving it to chance. As they settled me into the delivery suite, I began to relax and concentrate on keeping calm, putting any thoughts of the past - including Billy - out of my mind. That was until he walked through the door.

'What're you doing here?' I snapped. I could tell by his demeanour he had been drinking - possibly all day. He wasn't someone I needed around me. 'It's going to be ages yet - go home, go back to the pub.'

For the first time I saw Billy lost for words; he knew he couldn't argue with me. His face soon went from surprise at my reaction to seeing him, to annoyance because I didn't feel intimidated by him. I knew violence wouldn't be tolerated by the staff and they already had their suspicions about the bruising and weight loss.

'She's probably going to be waiting for some time, sir, so maybe you should let her rest and return in the morning.' Billy glared at the nurse who had dared to intervene on my behalf, having picked up my need to be away from him. Billy didn't speak to either the nurse or me; he immediately turned around and left. He couldn't have gone very far because at 2.20am he returned to find me in the midst of childbirth. Luckily he had sobered himself up a little, but almost immediately his constant barraging began. His attitude embarrassed me as he began to disrespect and insult the nurse, calling her a 'waste of breath'; the young male doctor who was overseeing the delivery in case of any complications was called an 'incompetent idiot'. Eventually the staff had heard enough, leaving me alone with him and only coming into the delivery room occasionally to keep a check on my progress. As in every delivery room, there are gas canisters containing oxygen for emergencies; sitting by the side of the bed Billy fiddled with everything and got out his cigarettes.

'You're not allowed to smoke in here,' I said calmly, not wanting to infuriate him.

'Why not - who says I'm not?' He retorted, his eyes squinting as if he was about to fly into a rage.

'They are gas bottles'. I made a gesture with my hand, pointing behind me as a painful contraction took my breath away. I knew what had upset Billy - it was the fact that I didn't get a message to him at the pub to tell him I was on my way to hospital and I knew he was biding his time until he thought he could show me his distaste. He began questioning me on why Anna was with my parents - how did I get her there and why I didn't want him at the hospital and how dare I tell a nurse to tell him to go away? His voice droned on and on, making the birth of my baby an ordeal. It wasn't that I refused to answer him; it was the fact that in the next ten minutes my baby would be born and my mind and concentration were needed elsewhere. In the throes of childbirth I could answer his ridiculous argumentative questions. To my horror, he lit his cigarette as he uncaringly watched me struggling to cope. My worries about the room going up in an explosion added to my state of stress. At that point I hated that man so intensely I wished it would blow up and end the torment I was enduring. The staff re-entered my room and immediately looked at Billy in disbelief. Billy walked out of the room to extinguish the cigarette. I was turned on my back just as Billy re-entered the room, but I was too busy to take any notice of him. During the birth, I was told to stop pushing; apparently the placenta was wrapped around my baby's neck. 'Pant, Jeannie,' I was ordered by the midwife; concentrating on her face, I joined her in the panting exercise while the doctor loosened the placenta. I was suddenly aware of Billy being so close to the right side of my face as he whispered,

'Fucking pant.' I held my breath and all panting and pushing stopped as I instantly felt the pressure of his hand on my upper arm. Even then, he forced his control on me.

Everything after that was a blur, until the sound of my beautiful Lilly crying made everyone in the room smile. She was handed to me immediately, the staff obviously aware of Thomas' demise. I saw the doctor push Billy away from me as he came to my side. I was in no doubt they understood the situation. Billy sat in the chair beside me for the next hour. With the staff gone and Lilly wrapped in a pink blanket and laid on my chest, I cuddled her in my arms as Billy sat in silence. Lilly was born at 4.31am. I was relieved when the nurse came in to take me to the mother-and-baby unit, asking me quietly if I wanted Billy to accompany me. I shook my head, my eyes said it all.

'I'm sorry, sir, but we are taking Jeannie and baby up on the ward now. You will have to leave until visiting time at 4pm today.' Her discreet smile told me she understood. Finally I had peace. Once on the ward, I placed my little finger in Lilly's tiny hand; she grabbed it so tight I knew then I would do anything to protect her. I was so proud of her, fighting to survive with such desperate odds against her. When I woke five hours later she still had hold of my little finger, it became something very special between us.

When visiting time came, I wasn't looking forward to Billy's appearance. I knew he would have been drinking; celebrating the birth of his daughter but drinking - which brought about his belligerent attitude. Still very tired, I watched as the three new mothers excitedly welcomed their husbands being bought flowers, chocolates and smiles. I wasn't jealous of them. I was just sad my life was as it was, but one look at Lilly and all other thoughts went out of my mind. I heard footsteps walking down the corridor and braced myself for Billy and his family. It was a pleasant surprise to see my parents coming down the ward with flowers, bags and smiles. Tears of joy filled my eyes as I realised they had left the anniversary party to come and see me and their new granddaughter. Just once in my dark days, I felt special. They had brought Anna with them to see her little sister. Anna ran to me and jumped on the bed to hug me. I leaned her forward to introduce her to her baby sister and Anna was overjoyed.

'Is baby coming home, mummy?' She asked, excited and happy. I looked in her eyes and as tears flowed, I simply nodded. Dean, my brother, and his wife Julia were also there which made me very happy. I realised I could hear the footsteps of Billy coming down the ward and my happiness was curtailed. I put on a brave face, not wanting my family to pick up on the tension between us, but I need not have worried. As they all had a cuddle of the new family member. Billy appeared. Instead of flowers, he slammed down four cans of beer on the cupboard next to me. We stared at each other: there wasn't any need for words. I knew he was annoyed at my family's visit. He stayed for a few minutes.

None of my family spoke to him and feeling brave, I joined in their ignorance of him. He left soon afterwards. Looking back, that would have been the perfect time to tell mum and dad the truth and with the suspicions of the hospital staff, it could have been the opportunity to escape this monster. But my life was what it was and I felt other people shouldn't be brought into my mistakes. I made the most of being in hospital and being safe, if only for a short while. Anyway, in my mind I thought he would be happy to be a father and end the violence now he had his own daughter. How wrong I was. After Billy had left, my visitors regained their jollity and mum opened the large plastic bag she held in her hands. She took out a selection of sandwiches, some trifle, cake and other nibbles from the party.

'Your grandma's sent them; you can't be there, so we bought some of the party to you. Grandma's waiting to talk to you.'

A nurse came around to my bay with the telephone trolley and plugged it in. Mum dialled my aunt's number and handed me the phone.

'Hello'. I heard the lovely voice of my grandma. 'Well done, a little girl, I bet she's beautiful.' The sweetness in grandma's voice choked me as I found some words in return.

'Thanks, grandma, I'm sorry I'm missing your party. I can't help it', I said with slight laughter. Returning the laugh, she answered,

'Don't you worry - you just rest now. I'm sure you need it. Take care, my love, and make sure you bring her to see me.'

I promised I would but never thought their introduction would be on grandma's deathbed; nor did I realise that would be the last personal conversation with my beloved grandma. Nor could I have known how Billy's control and violence would heighten over the next twenty months.

After convincing the doctor, against their better judgement, they agreed to discharge me from the hospital on the promise I would rest but with only two days to Christmas - I couldn't envisage much resting. Their concern for my wellbeing was apparent. Billy had not visited since my arrival on the ward, except for the initial first evening of his daughter's birth. After the delivery room ordeal, they knew they were signing a mother and baby into who knows what, but because I didn't tell them of the problems I was living under, there wasn't much they could do. I had, however, enjoyed the peace which solidified the bond between Lilly and I. Looking at Lilly, I knew with all the hell in my life she was my shining hope, if she could survive, then so could I. I rang Billy with the news of our release and borrowing his brother's car, he eventually arrived to pick us up. There was a young twelve-year-old girl with bright red curly hair accompanying him; her name was Tanya. He introduced her as Pete's niece and as I knew her parents, who were very nice people, I made her very welcome. He said she would help around the house until I was on my feet, and true to his word, she was a great help with Anna and around the house. For a while when she was around, Billy's attitude towards me was acceptable, though that wasn't to last for long. The house was clean and tidy when I entered 202 and everything seemed ready for the new arrival. The atmosphere was warm with coal burning on the fire, and I must admit Billy had made a special effort to make my return welcoming; he was friendly and concerned for my health. Both my legs were bandaged due to a problem that had arisen with the veins swelling. He allowed me to rest and he happily looked after his daughter. Though this pleased me, I felt a little uneasy with this complete turnaround of his nature. It unnerved me, as I was waiting for the real Billy to emerge. Within minutes of arriving home his family descended bringing with them two big white bags full of baby clothes, some bought, some hand-knitted. There was nappies, creams and various baby necessities everything I could possibly need for Lilly. I was very grateful and appreciated the parcels. What pleased me more was they hadn't forgotten Anna; a box filled with gifts for her showed me she was accepted as part of their family as much as Lilly. Finally there was one gift parcel left. It was handed to me as Billy's mother Vera said,

'Everyone seems to forget about the mother at times like this, so here are a few bits for you, Jeannette. Thank you for my beautiful granddaughter.'

Her kindness brought a lump to my throat I gratefully accepted the gift of a new white cotton lace nightdress and some bath soaps, bubble bath and perfume. I couldn't wait for the evening to come to have a bath and use my gifts. After all the visitors and well-wishers had left, we settled in for our first night together as a family. Billy seemed so in awe of his little girl. He couldn't stop watching her as she breathed and pulled little faces, scrunching her button nose and pouting her tiny lips. He was content. When all was quiet and Anna tucked warm and cosy in her bed, I headed off for my warm relaxing bubble bath. I lay for the first time calmly, thinking maybe all the violence might actually stop now Billy had the responsibility of being the father to such a beautiful baby. He seemed to have become human once again. How wrong I was.

On returning downstairs, I saw that Billy had moved a chair near the fire for me, so I sat cuddling Lilly. Dressed in the white nightdress and the short red dressing-gown mum had bought me years previously off the famous Carnaby Street in London, I felt nice. I saw Billy looking at me: the bruises had all disappeared and the rest in hospital had done me good. I tried to ignore his stare, unsure what was going through his mind, but hoped he was genuinely proud I had given him his daughter. The following day was Christmas Eve.

Billy rose early and suggested I make a list for the shopping. Surprised but pleased at his new attitude towards me, I checked with him that we could afford the amount on the list for the festivities. Happily he approved. Before leaving with Tanya he smiled, saying,

'Go and doll yourself up gal, we'll go out when I get back to show off our little Lilly.'

I saw a glimpse of the man I met - caring, thoughtful and friendly. The mood in the house had lifted as Anna and I enjoyed the happy atmosphere of Christmas. I hadn't much in the way of clothes, but rummaging through clothes put away for being too small, I found a pair of denim jeans and a sparkly top that I hadn't worn for a while. I knew my weight had plummeted over the last year, so I dared to try them on. The jeans were slightly big on me, emphasising my slightness, but using a belt to hold them up I felt pretty for the first time in months.

Waiting for their return, I was surprised by a visit from my brother Dean. He hadn't been up to the house since the Boxing Day party the year before. He didn't like Billy. He handed me a bag which contained a large joint of pork and twenty pork chops and a whole liver (he was a butcher by trade) and wished me a Merry Christmas. He chatted to Anna and had a peep at his new niece Lilly, after which he placed gifts under the tree - one each for the girls and one for me. He gave me a kiss as he said,

'Have a good one, sis,' as he left.

I remembered the Christmas after I left home at seventeen. I had got home from shopping on Christmas Eve to find that a bouquet of flowers, all in variations of red, had been delivered and left with a neighbour. The card said,

'Merry Christmas, Sis, love Dean.'

It made me smile then, as he had done now. Within minutes of Dean leaving, I received a visit from my parents.

'Mamma,' Anna screeched in her delight to see mum.

'Your dad's coming,' she said smiling as she entered the kitchen. I was relieved Billy was out. They bought presents for us all - even a token gift for Billy - and then dad placed a big box on the kitchen table.

'What's this?'

'It's your hamper you were paying for.'

'But I stopped paying mum and you gave me back all the money I had paid.'

'I know you did. I continued to pay it as part of your Christmas box, don't tell your dad,' she said with a wink. She also placed some homemade jam tarts, sausage rolls, mince pies, and a big iced Christmas cake iced sporting a Yule log and a robin (which I still have) on the top, were placed on the table. I hugged her and thanked her. She said, 'Your dad's bought you a couple of bags of coal he's putting it in the coal bunker. We will miss you this Christmas - you won't be with us but I can bring some of it to you. Try and have a good time.'

Leaving, dad smiled as he walked to meet mum at the door.

'See you soon,' he said as they left.

Deep down they knew my life had been intolerable, but they weren't aware to what extent. Putting the food away in the cupboards and the gifts underneath the Christmas tree brought home how thankful I was to my family. Around thirty minutes later I noticed Tanya struggling towards the house with a few bags of shopping. Nipping out to the gate to help her I asked, 'Where's Billy?'

'In the pub.' she said. 'He says for you to go up and take us all with you; he will be waiting.'

'Why has he left you to manage all this?'

'I said I could manage. Anyway he didn't get everything on the list, only what he thought you needed. I hope you're not angry with me?'

'Angry, why would I be?' surprised by the question.

'My mum would go crazy if my dad only got a few things.' Tanya was stunned by my calm exterior.

'Thank God for my family,' I thought.

There was no point upsetting Christmas for everyone by complaining, so we set off to meet him. I walked into the pub feeling so proud with my two daughters. I looked slim and felt pretty once more, as eyes gazed at the change in my demeanour. Instead of being happy to see me looking good, his glare and rigid face unsettled me. Nerves instantly rose in my stomach. Everyone made a fuss, as they do when a new baby is shown off for the first time. With compliments flowing of how nice or well I looked, Billy's face grew more rigid. Each compliment drew more nerves from within me. Being the centre of attention for whatever reason led to Billy's jealousy - Christmas would not prevent a violent outburst. I resisted any attempts at conversation, even about Lilly, until to my relief the rest of his family appeared. I spent the rest of the time hiding amongst them, keeping a low profile. It worked. On our return home (without Tanya - she went home earlier in the evening with her parents who had joined us to see our new baby and have a Christmas drink), he was in an unusually happy mood and though on tenterhooks I enjoyed the friendly atmosphere and the excitement of Anna. I told him that my parents and Dean had been up and what they had bought us. He didn't pass comment (I genuinely think to this day he didn't want to ruin Christmas for the children). While I was in hospital, he had managed to get a grant from the benefits office and bought us a double bed, so I managed to keep away from him as much as possible in the night. Even though sex was off the agenda after Lilly's birth, I knew that wouldn't stop him if the mind took him. I couldn't trust him, no matter how nice he was being. Lilly's cot was at my side of the bed, so I snuggled down on the edge of the bed and gave Lilly my little finger, which she gripped in her tiny hand. Before I could settle and think about sleep, I waited until I could hear Billy snoring - this was the sign I was relatively safe.

Christmas Day was a happy day. Billy seemed to enjoy the interaction with Anna as she opened her presents and - I will give him this - he had been and fetched her a lot of presents, including the latest electronic toy called Frogger. The two off them spent the morning laughing and playing with the game while I prepared dinner. We invited Shirley, our neighbour, in for dinner. Her family had gone away and she was grateful for the meal and company. Billy did go to the pub, but amazed me by coming home unusually sober. With a traditional Christmas dinner before us, we said grace and enjoyed the day. Billy seemed calm and content, but I knew never to take it for granted. I was fully aware how quick his mood could change. With the odd smile sent in my direction, I felt maybe this was going to be a nice day. After dinner Shirley had a cup of tea, a cuddle with Lilly and a few games with Anna. She stayed for an hour, then made her excuses and left for home, thanking us for a lovely time. Billy saw her to the door and home safely. I watched his demeanour as he re-entered the living room, wondering if, now she had gone. Would Billy's mask now slip? He got down on the floor and played games with Anna and when Lilly had gone to sleep after her feed and change, I joined in the games with them. I saw in him the man I fell in love with. That night, after I had put the girls to bed, he had a few beers and I had a glass or two of wine. We talked about the future and enjoyed the films on television. Sitting together on the settee cuddling, I dared to relax if only for a few hours: the beatings I had taken from him seemed a lifetime away. Deep in the back of my mind, though I strongly wished it would, I knew it wouldn't last. That night I had a good night's sleep, probably the only one since the night of the first attack.

On Boxing Day, Anna went to her daddy's for the usual

overnight stay, she happily kissed Lilly, Billy and I goodbye and off she went skipping up the path to meet Mark. My morning was spent tidying up and preparing to go to his parents' yearly party. On our arrival, the house was overcrowded with relatives anxious to see our new baby. Lilly was the centre of attention, being passed around for everyone to adore. Only eleven days old, she was oblivious to all the attention. I could see Billy was a proud father. I remember thinking 'maybe it's time to put the bad behind us and start afresh'. How stupid was that thought?

As it got to around teatime, I went upstairs to feed Lilly in a bedroom as I was breastfeeding and needed privacy and a breather from the in-laws' fuss and attention. My peace was broken by Billy's arrival,

'Why have you come up here?' he asked.

'Lilly wants her tea,' my reply accompanied by a gentle smile.

After changing Lilly, I gave her a cuddle and prepared to re-join the family. On returning to the lounge I sat for a while, watching everyone enjoying themselves. Looking down towards Lilly asleep on my knee, I noticed my breast had leaked milk. Discreetly making my excuses, I handed Lilly to Billy's sister and returned upstairs to change my top. I had come prepared with a spare. Whilst there I freshened up, reapplying my make-up and brushing my hair, as it looked like a long evening ahead. The music was beating loud in the room below and everyone was in high spirits. I was looking forward to a dance. I hadn't danced since the night I had met Billy. At that moment the bedroom door flew open and in he came.

'What're you up to?'

'Just freshening up, I had ...' I nervously carried on brushing my hair.

'Who's that for?' He angrily cut me off mid-sentence.

'For me I leaked a little, so I came up to get changed. Is that ok?' I snapped back.

'It's natural, you've just had a baby,' he continued in his annoyance.

'I know, but I don't have to show the world my boobs are leaking.' I put down the hairbrush and pushed past him, leaving him to lose the argument.

'Don't you walk away from me, you milking fat cow.'

His words caused a coldness to run down my spine. I knew that tone very well. I continued to walk downstairs to the safety of the family. Taking Lilly off her aunt Maggie, I sat down and kept quiet, knowing deep down he hadn't changed at all. His father asked me to dance; I couldn't really refuse the seventy-two-year-old man. Trying to be very careful not to upset Billy any further, Maggie took Lilly and I accepted his request, keeping the old gentleman at a distance. I could feel the burning of Billy's glare. As the dance ended Billy took my hand for the next dance; with a nervous smile, we danced. I have forgotten which song because of the words whispered in my ear.

'You slag.' His chilling voice bought back hard memories.

I knew he was preparing me for a good hiding that night. With his arms still tightly around me, looking to everyone else romantic. I knew I was dancing into the darkness of a night of horror. He gripped my skin on my back, digging in his fingernails which pierced my skin. I tried, but couldn't move from his clutches. His mother stepped in, having seen what he was doing, and he let go. I stepped back, picked up Lilly and made for the other room as he danced with his mother. Dave sat checking the horse-racing results in the newspaper.

'You okay?' He asked, looking deep into my terrified eyes.

I didn't say dare say anything in case I blurted out the truth of the last six months.

'You're not, are you? What's wrong with him now? He's never bloody happy. Just say if you need my help, I know he's a bully,' he said in a whispered voice.

Too scared to speak, I stoically watched the television while holding Lilly to me for comfort. It wasn't long before Billy appeared in search of me.

'Come on, we're going,' he ordered.

I didn't look at him. I knew Anna wasn't home, so I knew what to expect. No-one tried to stop us leaving - they kept out of it except for Dave. They were good at that, staying out of our business. All of them knew what Billy was doing to me. The family had all popped to our house from time to time and seen the results, but they said nothing. The walk home consisted of continuous threats and verbal abuse, the usual: whore, slag, the calling of my family, the convincing me I was worthless and that's why my parents didn't come to visit. I knew not to argue as this would only fuel his temper. His tactics didn't provoke an outburst of fear from me, so he began telling me he knew I had killed Thomas and he would kill me if I tried to take his baby away. It was a long mile pushing the pram up the hill home, trying to keep a check on my emotions. Showing any weakness would have resulted in a beating there and then. I kept quiet, I kept moving, until we reached 202. He waited till I had settled Lilly upstairs in her cot. I was dreading going back downstairs, but I knew I must. I didn't want Lilly hearing what was about to happen. I put a long-sleeved pullover over my thin vest top, so that the punches wouldn't hurt so much. I took a deep breath steeled myself and, with a trembling body, I went to receive my punishment.

His hand grabbed my throat the instant I entered the room. He kicked the door closed. I felt the thud of my head as it collided with the wooden doorframe, my feet losing the floor. Instinctively I closed my eyes. I refused to beg him to stop; I'd realised a long time ago he enjoyed my sorrow, so I kept quiet to get it over with. I felt the punches collide with my ribs, with each blow getting harder first into my left side, then my right. My eyes tightened a little bit more as I tensed up to lessen the pain he was inflicting. I refused to see the eyes of the monster before me. I felt his grip on my throat release, causing me to collapse to the floor in a heap. I lay gasping for air as I saw his foot, still wearing trainers, deal me a kick in the side of my ribs, winding me. I couldn't breathe. My thoughts were of my girls growing up without their mum. Still recovering from the birth of Lilly, my insides were already tender, so the pain intensified more than usual. I knew if not now then one day, I would die at his hand. After he had finished what he thought was enough, his parting words as he went to bed were a question I couldn't answer:

'Why do you have to make me do it?'

That night I stayed downstairs awake in the dark, feeling the swellings making their appearance and my face throbbing as it changed shape.

The Thursday after that episode, he decided we were to redecorate. He went up town to cash the benefit cheque and returned with a large tin of white paint, two rolls of embossed wallpaper and a small tin of bright red emulsion. I knew not to argue. We didn't own wallpaper scrapers so we started to strip the wall, which was council woodchip paper and was difficult to get off, with a couple of sharp kitchen knives. It took all day to make an impression on it. At 7pm, with still half of the wall to strip, he got washed and said 'you carry on - I'm going for a pint.' I gave the girls their suppers and got them into bed and continued scraping. It was a slow process, with half the wall to do on my own and me still weak having just had a baby and a kicking. I was still stripping it off when he walked in at 11.30pm. Of course he was, as usual, very drunk.

'Why haven't you finished it?' he demanded to know, 'and where's the girls?'

'They're in bed where they usually are at this time of night,' I replied in a quiet voice so as not to antagonize him.

He came over to me. Grabbing the knife out of my hand, he spun me around so my back was to his front and he held the knife to my throat. I felt it digging into my skin when I heard his menacing voice say:

'Who have you had in?'

'No-one,' I replied, trying to keep calm as the fear started rising from the pit of my stomach.

'Someone's been in - I can smell them. That's why you make the kids go to bed when I go out, you fucking slag.' His words were spoken directly in my left ear while he played with the knife on my neck. I stood perfectly still, but couldn't stop the eventual shaking taking over through fear. He started to laugh and said,

'I could slice your throat so easily, you're useless. What are you?'

'Useless,' I repeated, uncertain how to sound to appease him.

'You're a whoring slag. What are you?'

'No, I'm not,' I replied. The knife dug a little deeper. I started to feel my legs giving way as they shook beneath me. I felt the knife move from my throat. Suddenly I hit the wall on the other side of the room. He went to bed chuntering some derogatory words as he climbed the stairs. I listened to see if he had woken Lilly, but within minutes thankfully I heard him snore in his drunken stupor. Shaking, I carried on finishing the wall. Stripping it took most of the night, but I didn't want the knives in his view any longer. He got up the next morning to find the room prepared for painting, which he did over the next few days. The rest of the benefit money had been spent in the bookies and the pub, so he would be staying in the rest of the week. The room looked awful when he had finished it; red, 'the devil's colour, very apt' I thought.

It was the following May when I saw my grandma again, on her death-bed. I had received a message saying she was very poorly with cancer and not expected to live much longer. I had to get to see her and told Billy to get me there somehow - he did. I made my way to her room, holding Lilly in my arms. I walked into her private room to see she was surrounded by all seven of her sons and their wives. A couple of cousins were outside sitting on the chairs of the waiting area with my brothers. I nuzzled my way through the uncles and aunts with Lilly in my arms. I looked at my grandma and saw her smile at my arrival; with a weak and trembling voice, she beckoned me to her side.

'I knew you would get here, Jeannette. Come here, and sit by me.' The chair was vacated in my honour.

'Here she is, grandma, your new great granddaughter.'

Grandma's eyes steered towards my baby wrapped in pink. Grandma's face changed for a split second; the pain seems to leave her as she gazed at Lilly. Lilly, only five months old, returned her smile. Grandma guided her arm towards Lilly as I moved her nearer; grandma's hand touched Lilly's cheek. I regretted not seeing grandma earlier but she somehow understood why I hadn't visited. The look she gave me was full of love and her eyes smiled at me before her pain returned. Turning to my grandad, who was sitting on the seat the other side of the bed, she quietly said,

'My purse,' slowly gesturing towards the cupboard with her hand.

'You want what mother?' Grandad queried.

'My purse,' she insisted, a little more forthright.

'What the hell do you need that for,' said grandad as he passed and opened it for her.

'Inside,' she said again gesturing with her hand, too weak to act for herself.

He looked in and found one five pound note neatly folded. He passed it to her.

'For her,' she said, handing me the money. 'For her,' she repeated, adding 'not for him'.

I knew who she meant. I knew then she knew what I was going through. She had always been there for me and I knew death wouldn't interfere with our bond. Both my children were given gifts on their birth; on Anna's birth grandma gave her a silver coronation spoon for Queen Elizabeth II. I took Lilly's money and bought a silver baby feeding cup with the words 'To Lilly, lots of love, Great Grandma'. She died at 7.13am on the morning of May 21st. I was heartbroken. Two days later would have been her 73rd birthday. Her funeral was two days after that, on the 25th. It is a very solemn week for me every year.

Her burial took place in the cemetery at the top of the park opposite my family home. It was a very sad day. The wake was held at the pub opposite grandma's old house where they lived during my childhood; as expected, everyone was subdued. Billy was sitting to the side of me, keeping me away from the rest of my family. I had learnt to keep my emotions in check. I couldn't join in any conversations. I was so very sad, but I couldn't cry. I sat regretting the times I hadn't visited her because of Billy's possessiveness. I began to loathe him. That night, even he was concerned I hadn't shown any emotion.

'You are allowed to cry today,' he said bending down and directing it into my ear so it was unheard by anyone else. I ignored him. I couldn't cry. I refused to show any emotion at all. I locked the hurt away in my invisible secret box that was situated somewhere in my brain. A few days later I went to her graveside and broke my heart.

'Oh, grandma, what have I got myself into? I try to be good, but bad things happen to me. Help me please, please, help me.'

I sat for an hour at the side of her grave as Lilly slept soundly in her pushchair. I turned to leave. I heard her voice say to me:

'Stay strong.'

Suddenly I could smell the sweet scent of lilac drifting past me. I looked around there were no lilac trees in the vicinity. I knew she had heard me and was with me at that point in my life. I took her words and placed them within my heart. I had to stay strong for what was about to happen to me the following year.

Driven to Murder

I continued to visit my parents after grandma's death, although there would be long breaks from seeing them after a beating, so they didn't see my bruises. I knew mum hadn't been very well, so I would use that as an excuse to go down. Billy would agree but only occasionally would he allow me take Lilly. I would occasionally wait until he had gone to the pub and sneak down, but I wouldn't stay for long, making some excuse as to why I would had to leave. Mum would feed us when we visited; she could see the kids were fed but was worried about my weight loss, which had continued from before giving birth to Lilly. I had never been a slim girl but now I was looking gaunt and bony. If I arrived without Lilly mum give me food for her to take home, usually filling a bag full of necessities. I would take them into the house unnoticed and put them in the food cupboard, until one time when he accused me of sleeping with men to get money for food and gave me a good hiding. No matter how I protested my innocence, he always found for a reason to beat me. Mum would also slip me a couple of pounds to get Billy cigarettes, because the vile man took it out on me when he hadn't got any. I'd get them on the way home on the pretext she gave me the money to treat myself, taking it off me made it alright in his eyes. Only in desperation did I ever ask anyone to lend me a couple of pounds to get bread and milk. Mum gladly gave it me and refused to accept any repayment, understanding it would again leave me destitute.

He didn't hit me for a couple of weeks after the burial of my grandma, although the sexual violence continued. What hurt me the most was the fact that Lilly was in our room. I had learnt quickly to switch my mind off from the humiliation and pain. There was no point fighting anymore. I was very underweight and weak. I had no strength at all physically. He had browbeaten me into submission and, mainly so that the girls wouldn't hear or be frightened, I learnt to accept the rape and beatings quietly. There were many times through the coming few months when I would turn to Lilly's cot and find her standing in silence, watching what was happening. (Billy refused to move her into Anna's room. Though too young to understand what was happening - her sad eyes and subdued nature at these times showed me she knew I was being hurt). After a while my body became used to pain as my threshold lifted, but the thought of it being witnessed by Lilly hurt more than anything physical he could do to me. His possessiveness over Lilly began to increase soon after Christmas. Sometimes he would insist on keeping Anna and Lilly apart. My heart would break watching the two sisters crying to play with each other, but Anna soon realised I would encourage their time together once Billy was out - but she must adhere to his wishes when he was there. Keeping their play secret caused Anna to be very nervous that Billy would find out; the fear in her face became more obvious as time progressed. Anna was six years old.

There was little money living on benefits, and even less with Billy drinking and gambling it away. All I had to feed my girls and keep them warm was £4.24 a week in family allowance. Every Monday I would go to cash it at the post office, with Billy's orders not to spend it all. If I was feeling brave I wouldn't buy him cigarettes, spending it all on food, even though I knew I would be beaten, but at least I wouldn't have to go to my mum or neighbour for money. A kind neighbour named Pat would give me bread or anything they had spare; it was so demoralising, but I had to feed my children. It became rare for me to eat in the week running up to benefit day, hence the weight loss, but I knew the stress of my existence was the main factor for my frailty. Very often we hadn't electricity (we were fitted with a prepayment meter when the bills stopped being paid - this took 50 pence pieces) so I would toast the bread on the coal fire. The girls thought this was fun, but this dismal existence ripped my heart into pieces. My maintenance cheque from Mark came from the courts on a Thursday: accompanied by Billy, I would cash it at the local shop. He would then take it off me, going into the betting office and gambling it away. Occasionally I could get some shopping money out of the benefit cheque if he was in a good mood. It made me angry that women had children to feed but the government gave the benefits to men, leaving women to feed their children on a pittance: they had to beg, borrow or steal. On the odd occasion he was kind enough to give me money out of the benefit, or when he won at the bookies, he would throw a tenner at me to fetch food. Without argument, I would run up town as quickly as possible. I would order pre-packed coal to be delivered from the local shop, and get enough 50 pence pieces to last us in electricity until another payday was due, putting them all in the meter so he couldn't take them (until the day he busted it open and took the contents to the pub, leaving just one to refill the meter). Then finally I would struggle to carry as much food as it was possible to buy with what money I had left, which wasn't very much but was better than nothing. Buying clothes for the girls was impossible and I would rely on gifts or hand me downs. Mark would help by buying Anna's if she needed anything desperately, for example a coat or pair of shoes, but I got her things when I could and mum was a great help. It was hard, but there was no point moaning that wouldn't get us anything except a slap. I made the best of a bad situation. I would buy cheap meat and bake Cornish pasties or pies, filling them with little meat and lots of veg that was growing in the garden and freeze them for later in the fortnight. I didn't mind going without, as long as the children ate. One particular week we had nothing left in the cupboards or freezer to eat, the money had been lost on gambling or his drinking - the electric was about to go off and we were waiting for the maintenance cheque, which was late to arrive. Billy took to staying in bed when it was cold and we had nothing, not that I minded I was glad he was out of my sight. My hatred for him and the life we lived was increasing day by day. It was a Saturday when the cheque finally arrived. As the letter-box closed I heard Billy jump out of bed, running downstairs still fastening his jeans.

'Has it come?' His voice was full of expectation.

'It has,' I replied, 'but you're not having it - these kids need food and we need coal.'

'That's what you think,' he snapped back at me. 'Give it me,' he ordered, getting angrier by the second at the fact I dared to stand up to him.

I had hidden it in my bra when I heard him getting out of bed.

'Where is it?' he yelled, his face so close I felt his nose brushing passed mine. His voice grew nastier as his breathing hissed and sprayed over me.

'Give me the fucking cheque.'

I kept quiet, looking away from him, which made him worse. The girls were watching the one-sided argument and moved to the back of the room. They knew what normally came after the shouting. Anna ran out of the door and down the garden when she saw him grab hold of me. Lilly sat on the floor, taking it all in and keeping totally silent. His hands had gripped my arms just above my elbows, his yelling was escalating and his rage was intensifying. He shook me until I was like a limp doll. I didn't fight him.

'Now give it me,' he demanded, knowing perfectly well I wouldn't.

I said nothing. I shut my eyes and took in a deep breath to prepare for the expected punches. After a few minutes, I opened my eyes carefully to see why the punch I was waiting for didn't arrive. Billy stood before me, his eyes glaring and green. He was breathing heavily, either through anger or perhaps the violent shaking I had endured had exhausted him. I still said nothing. I was determined to feed my kids; killing me was the only way he would get that cheque. His face seemed flustered at the fact he was no longer frightening me into submission his eyes squinted until they were almost closed, as if thinking he was losing his control of me. Still, I said nothing.

'I fucking hate you, Lynn. Give me the fucking cheque,' he said in a last attempt to relieve me of it.

I had been with him for over two years, most of it pure hell, and he calls me his ex's name.

'I'm not Lynn,' I said quietly as I turned my eyes towards him.

I watched his expression change from anger to shock. He grabbed his coat and as he stormed out, he slammed the door behind him. I sat slumped in the chair where I had been thrown. Trying to come to terms with being called Lynn, It dawned on me that in his mind it wasn't me he was being violent to. It was Lynn.

I knew Lynn; she lived next door to my friend when I was fourteen. She was blonde-haired. We looked uncannily alike, even though she was around five years my senior. My friend told me she had watched him beat Lynn senseless in her parents' garden and police and an ambulance were called. She didn't know this man's name, but he was brutal to her. I didn't know who he was either, until now.

Anna came running in from hiding in the garden; she was tearful and scared after she had seen Billy leave. She was probably wondering what state her mummy would be left in.

'I'm okay girls,' I strained to say as Anna entered the room. She ran to hug me, clinging on tight through her fear. Lilly was just over a year old and tended to go very quiet during an incident. I had to somehow get the girls ready and go and cash the cheque, getting to town for food before Billy's return. Anna, being seven at the time, helped me with Lilly, and then got herself ready as I struggled up the stairs to the bathroom to freshen up and check no bruises were visible. One step at a time, I managed the task. The need to feed my children was more important than my condition. I managed the mile walk up to the town centre pushing Lilly in her pushchair, using it to support my aching body. Anna was doing her best to assist me. I felt very ill, but kept focused on the food I had to buy. On arrival at the supermarket - Anna pushed Lilly while I got a trolley. I wasn't buying much food; after coal and 50 pence pieces for the electricity meter I had about £4 to get enough to last till Monday - family allowance day. As I wheeled the trolley around the aisles of the supermarket with my few selected items, bread, potatoes, beans and eggs. I suddenly began to feel very faint. I checked to see where my girls were. At that moment all went dark. I had blacked out. Dazed, I came round to find I was seated in a chair outside the store on the pavement. Luckily an old friend of mine was in the store at the time and took care of my girls. Outside waiting for my revival, I saw their faces as my eyes began to focus and heard a voice asking if I needed an ambulance. Not quite clear headed, I replied 'No'.

I could see my children were safe and took a drink of water offered me by one member of staff who was concerned for my wellbeing. I sat quietly, feeling weak and confused. I heard my friend's concern as she said,

'Just look at the state of you. You're so thin, you're covered in bruises; please, get away from him, he's going to kill you.'

As I looked at her, she saw the fear in my eyes. If he found out about this, he would go berserk. I asked her not to say anything, but she replied,

'I won't, but everyone's seen you collapse. It's a small town: everyone knows what he is doing to you. You look dreadful, you're so different now. You're terrified of him. Go to the police they will protect you.'

'I need my shopping,' I said, looking around me frantically.

'They have it inside in the trolley. Give me your purse I'll go and pay for it and bag it up. Do you need anything else?'

'No,' I replied.

I sat for about thirty minutes until I felt strong enough to carry the food home. Anna pushed the pushchair as far as she could. I appreciated my little girl's help. All that was happening had gone far too far for me to stop it. I felt I had nowhere to run to be safe from him. I knew he wanted me dead and he was slowly getting his way. He had drilled into me that if I tried to leave he would blow my head off, sending Anna with me for the ride. In my confused and terror-based state my thinking wasn't normal. I knew he was violent enough to do what he threatened. He had drilled into me,

'While Lilly needs you - you're safe - but when she grows up. You're dead.'

Billy never made empty threats. I knew at that point, however bad the violence was, he would never intentionally kill me, well not at least for the foreseeable future.

I was pleased when Anna returned to school after the Whit week holidays. Like all festivities now, I counted on her having a good time at her daddy's. Every time there was a public holiday, Billy would spoil it by his drunken brutality towards me. We were all scared to enjoy ourselves, knowing it would be me who he would attack. The girls began to fear him although up to now he had never been violent towards them, they were scared for me. It was Thursday lunchtime during a visit to the club. Lilly, who was now around fourteen months old, was enjoying the attention as everyone made a fuss of her. The discussion was about Lilly and what a pretty little thing she was and how gorgeous her hair was, light blonde naturally curling into two ringlets falling gently on her shoulders. I was playing with her and chatting to the women, while the men played cards. Billy was losing heavily and I subtly pretended not to notice. One of the men playing cards said something to me. When I replied to whatever he had said, Billy turned saying,

'Shut the fuck up what the hell do you know?'

Embarrassed, I looked away and discontinued my conversation with the male card player. The man turned to Billy.

'Don't talk to her like that. She's given you a beautiful baby and you talk to her like she's something you've trod in. You should be ashamed of yourself.'

I was shocked that someone should jump to my defence, although I knew this would infuriate Billy and I would get the brunt of the anger boiling up in him. I lowered my head, as the fear started to rise in my stomach. Billy stood up and threw his cards on the table and stormed out of the club. I rose from my chair, being watched by everyone in silence, some knowing my fate when we got home. I struggled down the steps with the pushchair - someone offered to help but I dared not allow any man to talk to me after that. I was in enough trouble. I walked as fast as possible to catch him up, but he was almost home when I did. When I followed him into the house, he grabbed Lilly out of her pushchair and sat her in the middle of the living room on her little chair. I hadn't seen the scissors in his hands he began to hack off all her hair. I screamed at him to stop and leave her alone. I surged forward, only to see his eyes and the scissors held aloft pointing towards me. Petrified I stood riveted to the floor, too afraid to attempt to take the sharp scissors from him he was too close to Lilly. I feared for both our safety. Lilly began to struggle as she heard the clipping of scissors and the feeling she couldn't move her head, which was clasped tight within his hand.

Tears were streaming down her face as she shouted and cried,

'No daddy, daddy.'

He moved away from her. Her blonde curly locks lay around her feet. She looked at her feet and picked up her hair with her delicate little fingers. I ran to her, pushing him as I passed. I picked her up and comforted my crying baby until she sobbed herself to sleep. That was my punishment for daring to speak to a man. That night I lay beside him in bed, I turned to face his back. I moved 'til I was lying as close to the edge as possible. My eyes intensely studied his back, looking at every little detail of his skin in the light of the streetlamp. I stared at his shoulder blade. I knew his heart was under the left one and saw the shape of his muscles. My next thought was to shock me. He had driven me to the end of my tether. I wanted to end this horrific life my children and I were enduring. I started to have a silent conversation with myself.

'Have I got the guts to do it? What if he wakes up? He would use the knife on me, could I take that chance? Would I get away with it, driven to despair by his beatings? What about God, would he forgive me? Would I go to hell? Surely hell can't be worse than the hell I'm in already. I'm sure the girls will understand in time. At least he would be dead, gone forever. So I go to prison, maybe not. I could say it was self-defence; the police would believe me.' The more I thought about it, the more I convinced myself it was the only way out. My mind had taken over.

Creeping out of the bed, I picked Lilly up as quietly as possible, taking her downstairs so she wouldn't wake to see her mummy murdering her daddy. I didn't want her waking up and crying. I couldn't take the chance of anything waking Billy up out of his drunken stupor. I walked very slowly down the stairs, avoiding the one in the middle that creaked. The living room door was normally left open at night so he wouldn't hear the squeaky hinge that was strained through my continuous grabbing it to try saving myself from being dragged around the room. Carefully, I placed Lilly - still sleeping on the settee - surrounding her with cushions to protect her from falling off. I walked into the kitchen without the need to put the lights on: the street lamp shone through the open curtained living room. Quietly I focused on the knife drawer, my eyes searched for the sharp bread knife - the one Billy had previously held to my throat. I knew that one was sharp enough to cause the damage. But would it be enough damage to take him out immediately? Any mistake and he would retaliate, using the knife on me and then probably the girls. He had always threatened to take Lilly's life in a means to keep control of me. I knew if he killed me they would be the next target and Anna, how terrified would she be seeing and hearing it knowing she's next? Could I do it? I had to be sure I would go through with it. There would be no backing out for the sake of my children, not once I had begun this process. The knife felt heavy and cold to my unusually calm hand. Pushing the drawer closed, I listened as the cutlery rattled with the vibration. I stood silently - I heard the tinkle of metal echo around my head; still it didn't perturb me. Every move I made seemed to be in slow motion. I turned, my eyes fixed on the stairs door. My feet had a will of their own as they began to move one step at a time. I felt no fear. I walked through the living room, glancing over to check Lilly was still sleeping. Every step I made bought me closer to an action that would change my children's and my life forever. I had no doubt this is what I had to do. I made my way upstairs, creeping like a thief in the night aware all the time he might wake up. My ears glued to his incessant snoring. Again avoiding the creaking step, I concentrated on Billy's heavy drunken breathing which assured me he was deeply unconscious. I reached the landing, where I stopped to take in a deep but silent breath. I could see the doorway only a footstep away. I was at the point of no return. With the knife tightly gripped hidden behind my back, I prepared myself. I felt no hatred for him at this point, nor did I feel any anxiety, something that had been present since my first beating. I didn't feel anything at that moment. Even fear had left me. I moved forward to the doorway. I stared at the man I hated- worse- detested. I saw every inch of his face and it looked far from the face of the man - I thought I'd met. He had shaved off his beard over a month ago, showing the long, pock-marked, rough-skinned face that had become the face of my living hell. I imagined it pale with the blue tint of death, lifeless and void of expression. Then my imagination saw him wake as he felt my attempt to rid our life of this brutal man. The image disappeared, leaving the sleeping Billy before me. I knew I had to be quick. I had to pierce his heart in one thrust of the knife. I had to gather the strength from somewhere inside me. I moved slowly, quietly, around the bed, my eyes fixed on his face as it poked out of the bedcovers. I stood between the bed and Lilly's cot. Everything went hazy as my head felt a sharp jolt. I blinked to clear my vision, to feel Lilly's hand grasping my little finger. I looked at her as she smiled at me. 'Mummy,' she murmured her voice quiet and unsure. I blinked again in confusion. Where was the knife? I frantically searched around me, under the pillow, in her cot; nothing, it wasn't there. I don't know if I felt anger or relief that my mind had let me see what I was planning. I felt sick as I lay back down into the bed, realising that this monster was turning me into someone I didn't recognise, a murderer. I turned to look at Billy. My heart skipped as I realised he had turned towards me and his cold glazed eyes were open. He was watching me.

Our eyes glared at each other for a few minutes. Without a word between us, he turned over. I lay paralysed with fear, only this time I was afraid of me and what I was being driven to. I realised my conscience had given me a view of what my mind was intending to do. God had given me free will: it was my decision whether or not to take this evil path, to take this vicious man's life. Even if I got away with it, through extenuating circumstances, I had to live with myself. Billy's eyes had watched me; I felt as if he knew what was going through my mind. If he did, then it was only a matter of time before he decided to push me to it. As all the feeling of confusion left me, I knew I was better than that and somehow, some way, we would escape this monster. I prayed to God for forgiveness for even thinking this way. I prayed that he would deliver my children from this man, even if my path was to walk in darkness till I died. I said the Lord's Prayer continually for the rest of the time I was awake, hoping when the time was right the Lord would allow me out of this degraded life I was living. I woke in the morning subdued by the previous night's drama. Consciously, I had decided to do all I could not to invoke any more beatings. I would be quiet and submissive until my escape presented itself. I didn't know how or when, but I had faith it would come.

I gave up wearing make-up. If I wore it he would say 'who you wearing that for?' It would usually be followed by a slap. Then if I didn't wear it, he would still degrade me in some way for not looking my best. I couldn't win, so I didn't try. He once said to me that I looked a mess and threw money at me to go to the hairdresser's. That day when he returned from the pub, I had cut my long blonde hair so short it looked like I hadn't any left, just like he did to Lilly. He went crazy, beating me black and blue. He demanded the money back, but I had already gone to the shops and spent it on food. I had to tread carefully for the rest of the week. Shortly after that he realised I was getting immune to his beatings. I wouldn't flinch when he came near me. I wouldn't cry or beg him to stop. That was a big mistake; he found other ways of hurting me. It was a hot summer that year and he started to torment Anna, firstly as a game - but that's how he started with me, so I refused to leave her alone with him. That afternoon Billy and the kids were playing in the back garden and I was in the front doing a bit of gardening, getting a bit of peace. Tanya had been a regular visitor since I came home from hospital with Lilly, so I knew she would fetch me if anything was getting out of control. She hated Billy as much as I did. She came running into the front, screaming.

'Billy's dragging Anna upstairs to cool her off,' with an expression of panic.

I ran indoors. Hearing Anna screaming and fearing the worst - I ran up the stairs. Billy met me at the top.

'Stop,' he demanded.

'What have you done?' I dared to question him.

'She's just wet.'

I could see her coming out of the bathroom, soaking wet and sobbing. It transpired he had put her in a cold bath, fully dressed. I tried to push past him to go and comfort her. 'Mummy,' she cried when she saw me.

'Stay there,' he ordered, restraining me from getting to my daughter. 'Move down a step', which I did, all the time my eyes

107

on Anna searching to see if she was damaged other than being cold and wet. I told her to go into her room and change herself. I knew fighting him could be worse for her. He hadn't actually hit her, but she was very upset and scared of him. While my mind was quickly thinking of what he might do next, I felt his foot on my chest.

'Do you know?' he asked in a playful voice, 'if I was to kick you hard, I wonder how long it would take for you to reach the bottom of these stairs?'

My mind stopped listening to Anna's tears, as panic ran through it instead. I turned my head towards him, gripping tighter to the banister. He removed his foot. I could see in his face he thought it was funny. I felt a little relieved when the foot moved from my chest, but didn't bank on it returning full force with a powerful blow, causing me to let go of the banister. I flew backwards down the stairs, hitting each stair with my awkward descent, my elbows and knees hitting the walls as my head hit the banister before rebounding off the wall. Landing in the doorway of the front door, I smashed my face on the floor. I lay in a heap unable to move. I felt this was my end. I was going to die. Lying quietly and keeping still, I heard him run down to see if I was still alive. He got hold of my arm to lift my head and saw I was breathing; he dropped my arm, slamming it into the bottom step. I hadn't the strength to react. I sensed him brush past me, which made me shudder. I heard him go out and slam the door. Tanya came running in with Lilly. Seeing the state I was in, she took Lilly outdoors again. I heard Anna very quietly venture downstairs one at a time, afraid in case Billy was still around. She could see I wasn't moving. I heard her begin to cry as she cautiously descended the stairs. I couldn't imagine what went through her mind as to why I wasn't moving. Finally she reached me. I felt her sit on the bottom step; through bloodied eyes I saw her tear-wet face as I slowly forced myself to look at her for a slight moment. She took my hand softly in hers, her voice stammering,

'Mummy.' There was fear in her voice as she repeated 'mummy'.

I squeezed her hand lightly to show her I was hearing her. She stayed with me, holding my hand until I was able to crawl into the living room and climb onto a chair. I could feel the bruising appearing and my joints stiffening. There wasn't one part of me that wasn't in excruciating pain. Anna sat close beside me, trying to stifle her crying so as not to make me cry. She could see I was very badly injured; this time her mummy really had fallen down the stairs, with the aid of a foot.

'Look at your face mummy, it's getting very big.'

I knew she was referring to the appearance of the swellings and bruises. I could feel my lip thickening and blood seeping down my face. I had stopped looking at my face in the mirror a long time ago, as the face I saw looking back at me was becoming unrecognisable. I looked gaunt and ashen; I was so thin. A skeleton always returned my gaze. I couldn't stop the weight from disappearing from my body through the stress and anxiety which was my daily existence.

I asked Anna to fetch me a wet towel and then to shout to Tanya to bring Lilly indoors. I dabbed the running blood from my face and questioned Tanya as to which way Billy had gone. I knew he hadn't any money, so drinking wasn't an option. Stifling her tears at my pain, Tanya replied,

'He's gone out of the gate going downwards, down the hill.'

Instantly I knew he had gone to his family's home. Tanya helped me up and supported me in my attempt to walk outside. I needed fresh air due to feeling faint and sick. She helped me to the seat in the back garden, where I sat trying to pretend I was alright to the girls. Outside I couldn't think of anything else to do or say. I sat unable to speak. Around twenty minutes later, Billy's sister appeared.

'Are you alright?' She asked her voice sounding out of breath, she had run to our home. 'Billy said you fell down stairs - do you need a doctor?'

'No, I'm not alright. He won't stop till he kills me,' I said, fighting back the feelings of emotion. I refused to cry - grandma said to 'stay strong' and she always gave good advice.

'Billy did this?' she gasped. 'I know he's a bastard to women but I can't believe he's this bad. What did he do?'

'Put his foot to my chest and kicked me down the stairs.' It was difficult to mouth the words as my lips were cut and swollen.

This was the first time I had told anyone what he had done to me. I had broken the silence. Unfortunately, it was to his sister, so I knew he would get to know. I didn't care anymore. I had resigned myself to the fact he would kill me, and I would rather take the beatings than have him hurt my babies. She went indoors and made me a drink, which I couldn't bear on my lips. She stayed for a while to play with the kids, and said for me to go to bed and rest for a little while, but I dared not. If he came in and found me asleep, especially in bed, that could be the end of me. I didn't tell her this. I went back to my excuses.

'Did he borrow any money?'

'He tried but no-one would give him any. We asked where you were and he said you fell down the stairs. We were all mad because he'd left you. So, as usual, he is making everyone's life a misery up there. I called him a right bastard for leaving you, we almost came to blows, but Dave jumped in. Don't worry, he won't come home drunk. We wondered why he looked so worried, it's 'cause he did this to you,' she said.

'It's not the first time. He has been hitting me for ages and he will do it tonight when he comes back if he knows you know,' I said to her, still fighting back the tears.

'I won't say what you said, but you got to get him out of here; he's dangerous,' were her parting words.

'He's dangerous' I thought: and she thinks I didn't know that?

The terror of what he could do if I attempted to get away kept me his prisoner; he controlled everything I did. He owned me. He had systematically worn me down. I was only allowed to go shopping if I took the girls with me. I couldn't have a bath without Lilly being bathed in there with me. I could only bathe at night-time and only if he was in, otherwise I couldn't bathe; if I did, it was because I was having a man in when he went out. I had no peace at night after he went out, because he insisted Lilly stay up so I couldn't have men in. He even accused me of having men in and having sex in front of her. He was obsessed. He needed control over me and he had it. I was non-existent except for being my two daughters' mummy and that was the most important thing to me. Although at times, he wouldn't

110

allow me to tend to Lilly. He would make her cry just to see the frustration in my face as he prevented me from getting anywhere near her, or he would walk off with her as she screamed for me. It devastated me and made me feel an incompetent mother, being unable to protect her. It was all part of his game. I began to think he was driving me to suicide. He liked to see me scared - it entertained him. Once I had recovered from the stairs ordeal, he insisted on getting a babysitter and taking me out. I hadn't got anything to wear; my clothes were either ripped during attacks or had worn out through continuous wear. He gave me some money to go to town to buy a top. I did, not with pleasure but with guilt. If I hadn't it would have made him angry, so I told him the top was more expensive than it was and got a few treats for the kids, sweets and cakes because they hadn't had anything nice for a long time. It wasn't with excitement that I got bathed and ready that night; my hair was a little longer now so I tried to curl it, but it wasn't me looking back in the mirror. They weren't the eyes I remembered. There was nothing to look forward to except brutality after a night's drinking, so I would be walking on eggshells all night trying to calculate when his mood would change. Dave and his girlfriend were babysitting that night and they were staying over, so I felt a little more at ease that I may get away without being attacked. Even though Dave said I looked nice, I knew he was just being nice but no-one saw my inner self which was extremely traumatized. The night was as expected. He was being sarcastic to everyone and chatting up all the women in front of me. Though this didn't bother me, it made me look small in front of everyone. I dared not look or speak to anyone, especially men, even if I had known them all my life. Comments of, 'What's happened to her' and 'look at her hair, it used to be lovely' were apparent wherever we went. This didn't do my confidence any good, but what did I expect? A female friend of his came up to him and asked him what he was doing with a wreck like me. They talked for a while and she started staring at me and making me feel very uncomfortable. I asked him who she was. His answer was,

'She's the woman who's going kick your fucking head in, and believe me no-one can win her - she is the hardest girl in town.'

He smiled and seemed to enjoy frightening me. I don't know where it came from, but I said,

'Bring it on; she can't hurt me more than you have.'

He looked shocked at my verbal retaliation. As she walked over to me, I said to her,

'Do you have a problem with me?' My saddened eyes never left hers.

'Yeah, and what are you going to do about it?' Sporting a sickly smile.

I looked at Billy who seemed amused by the confrontation; he had obviously set me up. I thought 'well if I'm going to get a good hiding later it wasn't going to be because I was scared of a woman, after all, I've been fighting him for months.' My eyes returned to hers. With her inane smile fixed on her face, she asked,

'Well?'

'Outside,' I heard myself say and she duly followed me out of the door. Obviously everyone in the pub had been watching what was happening. The place went quiet. Everyone had known me as a friendly, bubbly, pretty blonde girl long before I met Billy - most of them were friends of my family. But now I was a bony skeleton of my former self whose hair had been hacked off and who was going outside to get her head kicked in. As we reached the door, I let it swing into her. I couldn't act scared, although inside I was frightened; not because of her, but because of Billy. If I got beaten, then he would beat me too for showing him up; if I beat her up, I would get beaten by him for not being ladylike. So I couldn't win, but at least I stood up to her, surely that would go some way to shut her up. Outside, she started talking: she wasn't used to people standing up to her.

'Just shut up and do what you came out to do,' I growled at her. 'I fight him every night - do you think you're going be a problem? Go for it,' the look on her face was one of puzzlement.

She said she liked me and always had done. My eyes never left hers. I could see that she was regretting forcing me to stand up to her. I could see she was actually frightened of my reaction to her threat.

'Inside,' I said brashly, annoyed that I had been put through this. She immediately scurried back into the pub. Following her with a scowl on my face, I saw her head towards Billy. As she passed him at the bar, I heard her say,

'She's alright she is, she's a good gal.'

I didn't look at anyone in the bar, not even Billy. I took my drink and sipped it. My mind was more on the journey home and when he was going to attack me. It would be on the street because Dave was staying over. He didn't like to have witnesses to his vented anger towards me. I remained quiet for what was left of the evening, hoping it would soon be over. As we left the pub, the woman shouted over to say goodnight. I ignored her. As we got to the top of our road, we saw a couple of people coming from the church hall.

'We have left-over food from our party, would you like some? It's fresh', said a small old lady, offering us two trays of various party food.

We accepted the gift thinking it would be nice for supper, especially with having guests. We made our way the top of the hill and I continued to head for 202. Billy asked for the tray of food I was carrying. I handed it to him, thinking he was going to carry it on top of his. He stopped walking and placed the trays onto the ground. Confused, I looked to see why he had done this then my heart sank as I realised he was going to attack me there and then on the street. I turned to him to face my punishment. He grabbed both my arms pinching my skin through my top as he lifted me up in his arms. I struggled to get free. After a few minutes, hoping someone would pass by and help me, the struggling stopped as I felt myself being laid down on the spikes of the railings outside the convent next to the Catholic Church where grandma's service had been held. I didn't speak: that was what he wanted, me to beg him to stop. I didn't. I felt him lower me slowly until the spikes were going through my top and the rounded points of the spikes hurt and pushed into the skin on my back. Rigid with fear, I stared in disbelief at his enjoyment at what he was doing. I didn't take my eyes from his, I saw them shine green and enlarge in shape.

'Look how easy it is: I've just got to let go and you will be dead, speared.' His menacing laugh was quiet and directed into my face as he lowered his face closer to mine. 'What a way to go, least you will make the papers.' The spray of his cigarette and alcohol-fuelled breath spread over my face. I tightly shut my eyes and lay perfectly still.

I was terrified but tried not to show it - this would only serve to increase his pleasure in my torment. The spikes hurting my back felt sharper as they indented deeper into my skin. The thought of being found dead entered my head as I thought about my children. I didn't show my fear: I lay quietly with my hands gripping the railings underneath me. My silence must have bored him, because he lifted me off the railings and threw me on the ground. Like a mechanical robot, I got up without reacting to the laughing bully. I began to walk as quickly as my aching back would allow, desperate to get to 202 and to the safety of his brother.

'Hey,' he yelled as I speeded up my pace. I froze until he caught up with me.

'Your tray madam,' he shoved a tray of food at me.

Taking the tray, I saw his amusement at the evening's events. On arrival home, Dave asked us questions about the night and if we had a good time. I said we had - he knew I was lying, but didn't pursue the conversation. Billy went to bed almost immediately and chose not to eat anything off the trays. I stayed up for a few hours with our guests, talking and enjoying the company and the food.

The next morning I had a raging stomach-ache so bad that I had to have the emergency doctor. It was Dave who insisted and rang the doctor. I had been vomiting for hours and had severe diarrhoea. I couldn't stand and with a bucket beside the bed, there I stayed. The doctor arrived and examined my tummy; seeing bruises, he looked at me in a knowing way. I looked away from him.

'You can get help for this.' He saw that I couldn't talk about it - I was in too much pain. He asked if I had eaten fish the previous day. I had eaten crabmeat off the party food tray.

'You have food poisoning. Drink plenty of boiled or bottled water and bed-rest for 24 hours.' I looked despairingly at him. He saw the stress in my eyes.

'Don't worry, I will tell him downstairs,' his voice was sympathetic. As he left the room I noticed his head slightly shake as he exhaled despairingly. I heard him leave and then Anna come running upstairs to comfort me. She lay a while and our guests stayed for the rest of the day to help with the girls and look after me. I slept most of the day and woke to see it had gone dark. Billy came up to see how I was; the sickness had calmed down, but I was very groggy. He said that the girls were tucked up in bed and all was quiet and for me to carry on sleeping. He was going out for a couple of pints with our guests and wouldn't be long. I honestly didn't care. I could see Lilly asleep in her cot. I turned over and went back to sleep. The next thing I knew was being jolted out of a deep sleep, with the smell of alcohol on his breath as he screeched,

'When did you buy it?'

Confused and still half asleep, I asked what he was talking about.

'Don't give me that, you fucking whore.'

'Billy I'm ill, leave me alone - I don't know what you're on about. I haven't bought anything except that top you ruined last night.'

He grabbed my arm and dragged me out of the bed. He continued dragging me along the floor, burning my legs on the carpet and banging me into furniture and doors. I was too weak to fight back. We reached Anna's room, where he pushed my face towards the underneath of her bed. He held me down as the barrage of insults continued. I could hear Anna crying as he continued to force my face towards a big cardboard lawnmower box shoved at the back of the wall.

'That.'

'Open it,' I struggled to say, I tried to break free of his angry hands holding my throbbing head. I started to wretch as my stomach began contracting. Eventually he let his grip loosen and I pushed him off me. I got myself to my knees and with the help of Anna's bed I pulled myself up and comforted her and quietly told her to go back to sleep. She hid her head beneath her covers, but continued to cry.

'Open the stupid box,' I repeated, feeling irate and ill.

He stood in the centre of the room staring at me; he eventually stormed out of the room. I stood for a few minutes. I knew he was waiting for me. I knew I wasn't strong enough to deal with a beating, but it was inevitable. Slowly I made my way to the bathroom; the diarrhoea returned, possibly because of the shock of being dragged from my sleep. Weak and exhausted, I looked at my face through the mirror - I washed my hands and said,

'Goodbye, face.'

I turned to stagger out into the hall, listening to see that Anna had settle back to sleep. I closed her door. He was waiting for me on the landing outside the bathroom door. He grabbed my hair in his hand and dragged me into the bedroom.

'I'll fucking teach you to buy things without asking me, spending my money.' I shut off. I needed to keep quiet so as not to wake and frighten Lilly sleeping in her cot. The punches to my stomach were more painful as it was tender from the food poisoning. I blacked out for a while, but as I became coherent, the punches were still raining down on me.

'Food poisoning, bullshit; you're just an idle cow, you're not ill,' he kept repeating with each blow. He didn't give me time to explain why the box was under Anna's bed. I was doubled over in excruciating pain. I started to vomit as I was thrown on the bed. He raped me. I hadn't the energy to fight him. Vomit was rising and returning into my stomach. I turned my head away; tightening my eyes shut and tried to concentrate on controlling the vomiting. I blanked out what was happening to me: he never took long and it was easier to get it over with. Force was a regular occurrence; I wouldn't willingly have sex with this monster. Trying to stop him was a losing battle and would only invoke an extra beating. After he had finished with me, I stayed still, not daring to move. My eyes still tightly shut I listened to hear his snore that seemed almost instant: it was then I dared to move and open my eyes. I turned to the cot to see Lilly standing up holding onto the bars. She was staring at me and, as our eyes met, she smiled a sympathetic smile. I didn't know how long she had been there or what the little mite had seen. I carefully got up to put her back in her bed, but I was so weak I couldn't lift her. I gently pushed her shoulders and she flopped down into her bed, she giggled and smiled up at me. I covered her up and got into bed, being careful not to wake the sleeping monster. Her hand was stretched out for my finger. I lovingly placed it in her hand; as she tightly squeezed it, she sighed and drifted off to sleep. Tears came to my eyes and I quietly sobbed myself to sleep.

As I expected, my face was an assortment of colour the next morning. My left eye was closed with the swelling. I found walking difficult due to the soreness in my stomach. How I survived that night I will never know. I returned into the bedroom to get dressed and to pick Lilly up and take her downstairs with me. As I got to the door I turned to check if he was still asleep: he wasn't, he was watching me.

'Just so you know Shirley gave Anna that box to keep her toys in. If you had opened it, you would have seen it full of toys.' But I knew he must have seen it before that night, or how would he have known it was there; it was just an excuse to exercise his authority over me and give me a hiding. His face didn't show any emotion at what he had done or what I had just said. That day he got up and started to get all of Anna's soft toys and began to burn them. We sat crying, as there was no way of stopping him. When the huge white fluffy dog that Dean had bought her came downstairs, I was going to get it off him no matter what: there was a stand-up fight over it. I refused to let go of the stuffed animal. The girls were screaming and feared what would happen to me. Anna was crying, saying,

'Let him have it, mummy, it doesn't matter.'

But it did matter. I decided he wasn't doing this to us anymore. He let go of it and I flew across the room with the strength of my pull against him. He ran upstairs and got hold of her big pink elephant that my dad had bought her on her arrival at home after her birth. The fight continued over this toy, and again I won. Repeating the run upstairs, he came down with my doll, the one my grandad had bought me when I was three-years-old. She had been put away in the cupboard above the stairs. This infuriated me and the battle over that was intense, ending up with the furniture flying and the kids running outside screaming, thinking I was going to be hurt again. I don't know where I got the strength from to fight for these inanimate objects. It was more the principle than the toys themselves. All the time Billy was laughing he thought it very amusing, but if I didn't fight for the doll, she would have been burnt before my eyes. I took it from him and he respected I had won, so he left the rest alone.

'I need a pint now after all this exercise.'

He walked out the house, never speaking to the girls; they ran to me for comfort, Anna half carrying Lilly as she was still unsteady on her feet. Anna hugged me and thanked me for saving her toys. I hid the toys in the cupboard under some old clothes, blankets and Christmas decorations. (I was later to find he had got rid of my grandad's doll: the elephant and dog were still there). I knew I had to get away, but how? Fighting him like that showed me I had the strength; he knew he was gradually losing his control over me. Things had to get worse before I could escape his clutches. I always thought of myself as weak to stay in this situation. I felt I had no choice, but if I was strong enough to survive all these beatings, I was strong enough to get away from him. I don't know how but the feeling he was going to eventually kill me was becoming a reality. The fight for survival was beginning to take over. The girls had begun to watch my every emotion they were okay as long as I didn't cry. The children associated pain with crying, so they watched my eyes. If they saw a tear then they would cry, especially Anna, and if she cried so would Lilly and we would all cry together, hugging each other. So I rarely cried. It was better to switch off emotion as way of protecting them. They had got used to seeing their mummy bruised, as did the neighbour Shirley and the other families around us. No-one ever mentioned the way I looked any more it was accepted as the norm. Shirley was afraid for me, and ran inside and locked the door when she saw Billy coming down our shared path.

Billy came home one afternoon with a little Norfolk terrier dog; the girls were ecstatic with their own dog to play with. Billy knew my family's connections to the dog world, and he knew I loved animals, especially dogs. Unfortunately the poor animal was just another way to torment me. He soon became violent to the dog. The little animal would scurry under the settee or run and hide under a bed upstairs when he sensed Billy coming home drunk. One night before he went out, he tied the dog up at the bottom of the garden, it was raining. He told me no matter what, if I fetched the dog in for any reason, he would kill the dog and I would be next. The rain got heavier and he started to cry and bark. I went down to him, but was too scared to bring him indoors. I was being watched by a neighbour, who sympathetically commented,

'Poor dog. Please let me ring your father to fetch you, we hear your screams. We hear what he does to you. Please, let us help you?'

I looked at them they could see I was terrified. I closed the door without saying a word to them. They had seen Billy tie our dog up outside but knew not to interfere. Then Billy came home; he was early and the dog was still where he tied him. I got a beating for being so cruel as to leave him out. He knew either way he had an excuse that night for a good beating. In hindsight I wished I had fetched him in, but I couldn't at that time take the chance that he wouldn't kill the dog before my eyes and say it was my fault. He was that cruel. He soon realised I wasn't going to let him use the dog to torment me, ignoring his games I knew he would get bored and leave the dog alone. After two weeks he gave the dog away which upset both girls, but at least the dog was safe and I knew the girls would get over the loving animal used as a means to hurt us with.

The life we were living had caused Anna to start wetting the bed. I kept it from Billy as long as I could. I didn't want him shouting at her. Eventually he found out by seeing the sheets on the line that had been on the previous day. I explained to him that all kids did it at some time and that it was only a couple of times. He started checking her bed every morning, causing her embarrassment and fear. He would shout at her and call her 'piss bed Annie' in public. The poor child was terrified. I told him to leave her alone it wasn't him who had to wash the sheets. He insisted that she should hand-wash them in the bath every day; I told him to stop being stupid, which got me another beating. He realised getting at Anna was a way of hurting me. He was getting bored with hitting me because I wouldn't fight him as I did in the early days. The fight was part of the fun for him. His attitude had changed towards Anna since the time he kicked me down the stairs, but I shielded her as much as possible, taking the beatings for it - rather me than her. We had been shopping one day and had been ordered to meet him at his mother's to walk home. We stayed for a meal, which made it late going home. I put the shopping on the handles of the pushchair, but because Billy was pushing Lilly, he took the bags off. He handed me two bags and handed another to Anna she was eight-years-old. I said that it would be too heavy for her. He instantly slapped my face like I was a kid arguing with its parent.

'It's okay, mummy, I can carry it, I'm okay, it's not that heavy.' She jumped to my defence. Billy strode off with Lilly and we followed as quickly as we could. I could see Anna was struggling and her arms were hurting. Seeing Billy in the distance, I swapped one of my bags that I had half emptied into the other bag. She looked scared as I handed her the bag and took the heavy one. I just put my finger to my lips and said,

'SHUSH.'

We continued to slowly follow the man in front, keeping a safe distance behind. He occasionally looked behind to check she was still carrying the bag of groceries. He slowed down to enable us to catch up, but we didn't want that. He noticed she was no longer struggling, so he came towards us.

'You bitch; you've swapped the fucking bag.' He grabbed a bag off me and threw the one she was carrying at me.

'Now carry it, or you'll know what will happen to your mum when we get in.'

Anna flinched in fear. He turned and walked off in front. This time he kept turning around keeping a close eye on us. Anna fell with the bag in her hand; she tried to quickly get up. I took the bag off her and again swapped it for the lighter one. I could stand his beatings; I was beginning to be immune to the emotional pain - and the physical pain would soon pass. Again he marched back and after immediately hitting me, he gave her back the bag. We walked slowly, I watched my little girl struggling. I told Anna not to worry about me, I would survive. She cried all the way home, but hid her tears as we walked in the open door waiting for our arrival. We placed the bags on the table in the kitchen. I found blood on the bag Anna had carried. I looked inside and found a pot of jam had broken when Anna had tripped. I looked at her to see her looking at her leg. The broken pot had jabbed into her ankle and badly cut her. I went crazy, shouting what a rotten bastard bully he was, but it fell on deaf ears. I said she needed to go to hospital to get it stitched, it was an inch long and was a V-shaped tear. It was bleeding profusely. He wouldn't allow me to take her to hospital, saying that I had to do the bandage, putting plasters and bandages on the table from the box of medical things in the pantry. I washed her leg and hugged her, saying how sorry I was.

'It's not your fault, mummy,' she quietly said, 'it will be okay.' I put my arms around her and cried. She had tried to be so strong for me. I did the best I could, promising that if it was as bad the next day I would take her on the bus to the nurse at the doctor's. She smiled and seemed happy with my comfort given to her. Over the last few weeks he had taken to threatening her with the poker used for the fire. Every time we came home she would run into the living room before us and hide it. If she didn't eat her dinner, he would put the poker in front of her plate saying,

'Make sure you eat it all.'

She had a habit, if she didn't want her food, of putting it behind the radiator in the kitchen. He never actually hit her with it he just used it to frighten her. On one particular night we had been out, she could tell he was in his bad mood. She ran into the house and into the living room, dived for the poker and hid it behind the settee. I saw what she did. I tried to get her in bed quickly, but he was having none of it. He sat on the settee and told her to sit next him. Nervously, she did as she was told. I sat opposite, keeping a close eye on what he intended to do. He started taunting her while looking for the poker. He was saying she was smelly and dirty because she wet the bed; what he didn't realise was that, the more scared she got of him, the more she wet the bed. Unbeknown to him, I had the radio cassette next to my chair as he started in his taunts, I pressed the record button. If I had openly defended Anna it would have been worse for her, so when he called her I had to join in, all the time hating myself for what I was saying. It was the only way to protect her:

if he thought he wasn't upsetting me, it wouldn't be any fun for him and he'd stop. I hoped with all my heart she understood why I had to let him think I agreed with him. He was looking for the poker. Knowing the tape was running, I asked him if he was looking for the poker, so it was on tape because then people would believe me. He couldn't find it. Anna eyes never moved off mine. I could see her trust in those eyes. Eventually he got bored and said, to our relief, to take her to bed.

'Come on, Anna,' I said getting up from the chair. I gently smiled to ease her fear and kept an eye on the ever-changing expression of Billy's face. Reaching for her outstretched hand, I pulled gently on her fingers until she gradually got to her feet.

'Come on,' I repeated as I felt her grasp my hand tightly. I drew her close to me, her eyes still fixed to mine, and we slowly made our way to the door hoping he wouldn't stop us. It was 1am and Lilly had already been put to bed, so getting upstairs unharmed was imperative. As we got to the door, Billy said,

'No wetting the bed tonight or you're going to get a smacked backside.'

Though we both heard his warning, we continued to walk towards the stairs in complete silence. I took her to bed. Tucking her in, I kissed her and said as I held her,

'I won't let him hurt you.' She snuggled down and closed her eyes.

It was a promise that was to haunt me forever. I checked Lilly was sleeping and comfortable and I got into bed, as always on the very edge. I heard Billy switching the lights off downstairs, so I closed my eyes hoping he would just get into bed and give me some peace. As he entered the door he said,

'If she's wet in the morning, you're to smack her and if you don't, I will.'

I didn't respond, although I knew he meant it. Within minutes he was snoring. I sighed with relief and prayed that Anna's bed would be dry the next morning.

It wasn't.

'You better do as I said, or I will', he shouted from the bedroom.

I couldn't hide it as he would check - and life would be even more hell than usual. We looked at each other with tears in our eyes. I took off my slipper. We knew we had to get it over with. Half smiling with dread, her little lips trembling trying to not to cry, she turned around (mum gave me the slipper lots when I was a child and although it stung for a while, there was no lasting damage). I hated myself so much at that moment (this hatred continued for another 25 years) but it was better for Anna for me to do it lightly than Billy beating her. I gave her a whack with my slipper, and she cried out. The door flew open banging into her bed. I was grabbed from behind and thrown out of the room, with the door slamming behind me. The force with which I was thrown caused me to land at the top of the stairs. I quickly got to my feet and rushed the bedroom door. Hearing the bastard beating Anna, I banged and pushed, screaming at the top of my voice for him to stop and leave her alone. No matter how hard I pushed, I couldn't get the door to open. Her screams were loud and painful. I frantically tried to get to her, but something was blocking the door. I bent the door handle in an attempt to open it, as she screamed for me to save her. I was helpless. I kept pushing and pushing the door the handle was cutting into my hand but it wouldn't open. Lilly had heard all the commotion and joined in the screaming; it was mayhem. Eventually the door flew open, forcibly swinging wide on itself, causing it to smash into the end of Anna's bed, rebounding immediately, causing the sharp edge to hit me on the brow of my head. Dazed, I lunged towards Billy, pushing him into the wall and away from Anna who was cringing in terror from the abusive ogre. Placing my arms around her, I shielded her from any further assault. I turned to face Billy - he was recovering from his unexpected clash with the wall.

'What have you done - you bastard?'

'That's how you punish the kid,' and he stormed out of the bedroom.

I cuddled Anna in my arms; I begged her to forgive me. Her bottom was already swelling into the shape of a handprint as it bruised. She was in severe pain, but trying to sob quietly in fear of Billy returning. Every noise made her jump. Then it hit me: he wasn't drunk. This time it wasn't the drink making him do this to us drink was an excuse. My heart shattered into a million pieces as I realised I must get my little girl out of here even though it meant losing her, she had to be safe. I held Anna tightly in my arms as her tears soaked into my cotton top. I knew what must be done, though it tore at my heart. Sitting on her bed trying to comfort my damaged child, the hatred I felt consumed me until I felt void of emotion. Eventually Anna was calm enough for me to dress her. I promised he would never hit her again; this promise I kept. The realisation of how far he had gone in beating Anna seemed to strike fear into Billy. He may have browbeaten me into keeping quiet about his vicious bullying, but he had no control over Anna once she was away from home. He knew the following Monday she had school and as it was only two days away from her usual visit to her daddy's, he feared his abuse was finally to be discovered. For the rest of that day Billy kept very quiet and to himself for which I was grateful. I kept Anna away from him, taking Lilly with us upstairs into Anna's room to play with toys or in the kitchen, anywhere as long as she didn't have to look at the evil monster. All my thoughts were how I was going to explain to her she was going to have to leave me. I knew this would break her heart but deep down I knew her safety was paramount and that now he had injured her once the pattern of abuse would continue. It was a very long day full of sadness and hurt. After I had settled the girls into bed I returned downstairs only to face Billy's attempts to control the situation.

'She's not to go to her dads this weekend.' His words returned to the dominating tone that I knew so well. 'You're to ring his mam's and tell them she's poorly.'

'And school?' I replied in a nonchalant manner. 'We keeping her off there as well until her bruises heal? What shall I tell them; that she will be back in around three months' time, because that's how long before those bruises will heal' I stared into his eyes, not caring if he attacked me. He looked away from me, his face looking stressed and worried. Silence filled the room. Eventually Billy left the room. I didn't bother to wonder where he had gone. I looked for the radio cassette and, making sure he wasn't re-entering the room, I pressed the eject button. Nothing happened. I pressed it again - still the machine didn't eject the tape I had caught Billy's threatening behaviour on. I lifted the radio and checked it for the tape. It had gone. My heart skipped a beat as I realised Billy must have taken it after we had gone upstairs the night before; my evidence had gone. I wondered how long it would be before it turned up. I knew he would use it when he couldn't find a reason for a beating. I sat quietly, deep in thought, until he returned from where he had been. I started to plan my escape, which would allow me to take the girls safely with me.

'She's not going to her dad's,' he repeated as he walked into the room.

'Yes, she is,' I calmly stated.

'Well, they will blame you for it because she's yours and now they will realise what an incompetent mother you are.'

'To bring her into this violence, I must be incompetent. I don't deserve to be her mum.'

'And Lilly, don't you think they will take her off you when you're put into prison for child abuse?' His tone had mellowed as he realised he lost his immediate control of me. I could see he was in panic.

'Me? You did that to her, not me.' I felt a slight sense of anger rising but tried to subdue it, as it always resulted in my face being distorted by his iron-clad fist.

'Your word against mine,' he said with a scowl 'if you was to tell them you did it, Mark won't take it any further - you know he still loves you - so nothing else will be said. If you don't and the authorities get involved, Lilly will be put into care 'cause everything will come out. How do you think people will think when they know you put her in danger?'

I couldn't believe what he was doing - he was convincing me to take the blame for the sake of Lilly. Little did Billy know - I was going to take Anna to her daddy's on Sunday and I wouldn't be coming back to 202. I intended to beg Mark's forgiveness in the hope that he would help me. I now had proof of Billy's violence.

'If I can't have Lilly, no-one can.' His tone now turned menacing as he glared at me. I saw the greenness in his eyes appearing. Though I tried to stay calm, the fear began to well up in me. I tensed my body and gritted my teeth as his barrage of blame lay on me. Though everything he said was lies, I began to feel I was to blame. Inside I knew I was to blame for not escaping that first time he hit me, when I was four and a half months pregnant. The shame was mine - he was right, it was my fault.

Sunday morning arrived and although he had been trying to be friendly towards Anna, she wouldn't speak or interact with him. I didn't ring her grandmother to say she was ill; instead I went upstairs and packed her school uniform, her books and a few of her favourite dolls - into a bag. I couldn't put her through this anymore. Her injuries were too much to bear and if it meant prison for me then so be it: at least then I could get Lilly to safety. I knew my mother wouldn't let her grandchild go into care. My mind was set.

'Anna,' I said as she came upstairs to find me, 'come here, sweetheart, I need to talk to you'. She limped into her room where I had been finding her clothes. 'You know mummy loves you very much.' I steeled myself to stop the trembling of my voice. 'Sometimes things get really bad between adults and the safety of their children has to come first.' She nodded her head. I noticed how blonde her hair was tied up into a pony tail and the thought of never brushing her hair again welled over me. I swallowed deeply and put her carefully onto my knee. 'I want you to promise me one thing, Anna.'

'Anything mummy.' Her innocent voice was saddened and confused.

'You're going to your daddy's today as normal. Now when he sees what has happened to you, I need you to promise me you will tell him that...' I stopped for a moment, disgusted with myself, 'I did it to you.'

Bursting into tears she cried, 'but it wasn't you, mummy.'

I held her as tight as her fragile body would allow me. 'Shush, shush, I know that and you do and that's all that matters, but it is my fault, sweetheart and I must take the blame for it.' As tears ran down my face, I continued, 'please promise me you will say I did it.'

'Okay, mummy, I promise.' Her arms around me were warm and undeserved. 'Doesn't Billy like me anymore? He hasn't liked

'She looks well, don't you think?' He said with a laugh in his voice. I ignored him. 'Don't you want to see her?'

He taunted me for the rest of the evening. I didn't let him think he was getting to me. I found the strength to find a stoic expression. I knew Anna and Mark knew I hadn't beaten her and that was what counted to me. People knew that this relationship was soon going to end, but the question was, how? We were quiet when we walked home; he knew he was safe and that I hadn't said anything to anyone and that I was taking the blame for her attack. Little did I know it was all part of his plan to show me off as a violent child beater, so that no-one would believe me if I decided to tell the truth. He knew he had total control over Lilly and me. Comfortable knowing I had no-one left to turn to, he started leaving Lilly with me. This was my special time with her for the few hours. She started to become a very sad baby who clung to me for love and warmth. When Billy came home he would take her from me and only allow me near her to feed or change her. He tried everything to break the bond between us, as he had done with Anna. He was trying to send me crazy. I knew he wanted me out of the way, so he could live in my house with his daughter. I focused on the day I would get Anna back but, before I did, I had to get rid of him. My thoughts turned dark towards him: it was going to be 'kill or be killed'. I knew I couldn't take much more and I certainly wasn't going to allow him to be in sole control of Lilly; her life would be a living hell and no-one deserved that.

My mind began to explore ways of getting away. I hadn't any money. I couldn't use the shopping money; since Anna left, the child benefit had reduced by half and the maintenance had obviously stopped. Two pounds twenty five pence wouldn't get me anywhere, and anyway, I needed that to feed Lilly. I couldn't go to friends; I felt I hadn't any. My family seemed to have forsaken me after Anna's ordeal. Then one August morning I had an invitation through the post - to my niece's birthday party. It was her second birthday and all the family, including Anna, would be there. It was a frightening thought having to face everyone, but it was my only chance to get away with Lilly - hopefully if Anna still loved me, it would give me strength to get help. Maybe this was my escape. I mentioned it to Billy; he couldn't really say no because that would alert my family to the depth of his control.

August 15th arrived. I dressed Lilly in her best dress and with trepidation I walked up to my brother's house. Everyone as expected was there. I gave my niece a card and a small gift I managed to get cheaply. I walked into the lounge to see Anna sitting with her three toddler cousins - she looked so different. Her lovely long blonde hair had been cut shorter and though it pleased me to see she was smiling, I felt incredible guilt.

'Anna, Anna,' Lilly excitedly shouted as she ran to her big sister. With a lump in my throat, I decided to leave them together. I had said 'hello' to Anna but the atmosphere was awkward and though the family tried not to react, I felt all eyes on me. I smiled at her and her smile back made me feel still loved. Looking at her I felt she didn't need me anymore - she was in new clothes and looked healthy. This pleased but also saddened me. Dejected, I made my way into the kitchen where I found a chair in the corner of the room next to the table and sat down. Everyone was drinking beer or wine. I loathed the smell of alcohol it being the source of my pain, so I asked for a cup of tea. For all my attempts to look nice, they could see my faded jeans had almost worn through into holes and that the vest top was baggy, showing my protruding skeletal frame. The conversations were strained as they tried to engage me in small talk. I felt so much emotional pain seeing Anna and being with my family that I couldn't speak or find the words to say. I felt an alien in my own family. I didn't want to be emotional and spoil the atmosphere of my niece's party, so I sat cringing into the corner and drank my tea as everyone was nattering between themselves, the sound of their voices blending into one loud blurred noise that began to hurt my head. I felt faint, my heart was thumping, and I found it hard to focus on anything or anyone. They must have sensed that my illness had obviously gone beyond my control. I needed to handle being the outcast of the family, the child beater. There was so much food and my hunger was causing loud growling sounds from my stomach, but I couldn't eat any of it. After my tea I drank tap water and stayed in the corner left alone, while the family were in the other room enjoying the child's party.

After a while both sisters-in-law Ellen and Julia came into the kitchen and pulled chairs up to the table, sitting closely either side of me. I smiled the best I could though I felt alone, and my smile was knowingly false. Ellen said to me very quietly,

'I'm not going to ask you if you are alright because it's plain to see you are not. If he is being violent or even just saying nasty things to you, there is somewhere you can go. Here's a number - if you ring them they will fetch you and protect you and Lilly.'

Julia took hold of my hand which was resting on the table.

'You're shaking - please let us help you - take the number.'

'Shall we ask Darren and Dean to go down and fetch your things? I will ring for you, get you safe.'

All this concern was too much for me to take in, it was like my mind couldn't take in what they were saying. I said nothing in reply. I pulled my hand from Julia's and cringed even more into the corner. I knew they were trying to be kind, to be helpful; but in my confused state of mind - Billy was a vicious monster and I couldn't have coped with the guilt if he maimed my family. Getting them involved in my mess would cause more anxiety for me if either of them got injured knowing it was my fault. Infuriating Billy always made life - even harder for me. I decided to keep silent. I refused to go into the party and asked if I could sit there until it was time to go back to 202. Ellen said that was fine, and though they ignored my emaciated bruised body, I knew my secret was out. I sat for an hour and a half in the kitchen thinking nothing, just contemplating the peace of being alone. I was a walking skeleton with drawn pale features and my family was having fun in the next room. Maybe it was selfish to feel like this but I felt alone in this world and this confirmed it. I felt I should leave but I didn't want to upset anyone, least of all my girls. Lilly needed to be loved by her family, even if I didn't deserve to be. I sat trembling (which was a normal reaction in my daily life) knowing that when I got home he would probably get angry with me and I would take more pain to my body. I knew I was getting to the point I couldn't handle anymore; desperation wasn't far away. The door opened and in came a very frightened little girl. Looking at me she cried,

'Mummy.'

I lifted my head to see Anna's tearful eyes looking at me. I lifted my trembling arms and she rushed into them, we both hugged and sobbed.

'I'm sorry, mummy.'

'Sorry for what?' I asked gently.

'Daddy wouldn't believe me when I said it was you, that's why I didn't speak to you when I saw you in the club. I thought you would be mad with me.'

We both continued to sob as her arms held me tightly around my waist.

'It's okay, it's okay. I think your daddy knows me a little more than I thought. Nothing is your fault, Anna, always remember that. I promise I will make it alright. I'm trying to now, and now I know you still love me, I promise, soon it will be all over. Just remember, anything I do is never your fault.'

We were left alone for a while by the family and we used our time to hug and be close. It was a ploy by Ellen and Julia to bring us close again. It worked. Wrapped in my arms she asked,

'Come into the party, come and sit with me and Lilly?' Frightened of everyone's reaction, I first refused her request. She moved slightly away from me, outstretching her arms. Getting hold of my hand and pulling me she begged,

'Come on mummy, please?'

I couldn't refuse her and we walked into the family hand in hand and her with a big smile on her face. I'll treasure that smile, always. I cherished the time we spent together. I knew there was a chance that I might not be around much longer, so seeing all my family, even though they were distant towards me, meant everything to me. After an hour in the party room – I realised the atmosphere was strained as none of my immediate family knew how or what to say to me – I made my excuses, I and Lilly left for 202. On leaving Ellen accompanied me at the door, she asked me to take the number and to consider everything she had said. I refused the number. Things had gone too far for outside help, but I did appreciate her trying.

Anna loved me. I knew that now and I knew I wasn't worthless; I was her mummy and I needed somehow, some way, to 'stay strong'. I walked back to the house of hell my mind began to find a strength I hadn't envisaged possible. I knew what I was going to say. I knew I could fight this monster. I needed to. I needed my Anna with me. I was her mummy. The nearer I got to 202, the stronger I felt. I threw open the gate and let it swing loudly shut. I barged through the kitchen door, making as much noise as possible. I needed him to know the frightened wreck of a woman he kicked; punched and abused in every way possible had found some self-respect. I lifted Lilly out of her pushchair and handed her to Billy saying,

'She's tired. When she's had her super she is going to bed.'

He didn't argue. He glared at me, wondering how I dared speak to him in that tone. I ignored him. After her supper, I did indeed walk her past him and take her upstairs. I wasn't stupid I knew at any given moment he could follow me and attack me, but other than attacking Lilly he couldn't emotionally hurt or blackmail me any longer. I returned downstairs, with an assertive voice which hid my trembling inside. I informed him:

'I will be sleeping in Anna's room from now on. I'm not having this anymore. This is my house. You have one week to get out, if you don't, I will ring the police to get you out and I will tell them everything and I mean, everything. Goodnight.'

I walked upstairs calmly when all instincts told me to bolt as quickly as possible. I didn't want him to sense how scared I really felt. With each step I expected his hands dragging me back down. Before walking into Anna's room, I glanced to see Lilly was sleeping. I locked myself in Anna's room, putting a cupboard up to the door to keep him out. I knew he hadn't been drinking, so knew he wouldn't use his own daughter against me - after all that's what he wanted: Lilly without me. In my heart I knew she would for now - be safe. As I lay fully clothed on top of Anna's bed I thought about the look of shock on his face as I made my demands. I waited for the bang at the door as he tried to break in but it didn't come. What did come was a knock. He spoke more softly than I had ever heard him speak. I knew it was a ploy to get me out. For one night I needed to be alone to think and decide how I could escape this monster. Without the help of my family it was going to be harder, but I did now know there were places for women like me.

'Please. Come out and we will talk.'

I ignored his feeble attempt to win me over. I thought that Darren and Dean would be angry after seeing the state of me. Ellen had asked me if I wanted her to have a word with my brothers and send them down to sort him out, but I had refused her offer. I had come this far without their help; I would end this myself. For an hour I listened for the gate slamming shut and both Darren and Dean making their presence known. I waited to hear their footsteps coming down the path. Many times after a beating Billy would say,

'Now fetch your brothers.'

'Never,' I would reply, but it didn't stop me wishing and praying that they would come and throw him out and rescue me. They never came and this time was no different.

'Why should they get hurt through my own stupidity?' I consoled myself, but talking to my sisters-in-law had given me a little confidence; at least now I knew somebody cared. Billy eventually realised for all his pleading, I wouldn't open the door. Not having money for drink for two weeks gave me time to empower myself against him. Anna was my main driving force. The following morning I ventured out into the hall very carefully, after all he had beaten Anna when sober. I looked into the bedroom; he wasn't there, neither was Lilly. My heart sank. I heard Lilly playing with her toys as I crept downstairs, she was laughing and Billy was joining in the play. Picking her up and kissing her good morning, I kept my eyes away from Billy's, Lilly was happy to see me. He spoke quite politely,

'She missed you when she woke up and you weren't there. She asked for you.'

'Did she?' I replied in a matter-of-fact tone. There was no use angering him by not speaking, though I was determined not to be friendly.

'How did the party go?' He asked.

'Okay, we enjoyed seeing Anna.'

'How was everyone with you?' I could tell by his manner he was afraid I had told them the truth.

I didn't embellish on the meeting and continued drinking my morning cup of tea. I gave him short and to the point answers to any queries or conversations he attempted to make for the next two weeks. In that time I felt a little more in control of myself and began to see how scared he actually was. He knew he was close to losing his control of me. I carried on with the routine at night-time. As soon as Lilly was in her cot, I would go in the bath and then into my room, always remembering the cupboard so he couldn't get in. It was nice to have a bath on my own, but still I could never allow my mind to rest; that would be stupid. The day before the benefit cheque arrived, he knocked on Anna's door and begged,

'Let's give it another chance neither of us wants to lose Lilly.'

'I didn't want to lose Anna,' I retorted.

There was a family party to be held at a club a couple of towns away and he convinced me to go, saying it would be a chance to talk about things. The family would be there so I needn't worry about him hitting me. He realised I meant what I said and things had to change. He asked politely, and seeing as his attitude had been different and he promised Dave and his girlfriend could stay after babysitting. I stupidly fell for his lies.

True to his word, Billy was the perfect gentleman and left his attitude of belligerence at home. Though still wary of him, the night went well. Feeling safer with Dave and Elizabeth staying over, I wasn't afraid of returning home with Billy. Dave said it was nice to see me happy for once, which encouraged a slight smile from me as I told them about the party they had missed. For some unknown reason Billy insisted on having a bath, which was out of character after drinking. He disappeared upstairs to run the water. I continued to laugh and chat with our guests. After a few minutes, Billy shouted for me to come upstairs. Thinking it might be Lilly who was awake, I went upstairs smiling, feeling good; he stood by the bathroom door.

'When was this done?' He asked. He was talking about the new pull cord to the bathroom light, which had been replaced by the council repair man the previous morning.

'Yesterday morning,' I replied, still smiling.

'What while I was in bed?'

'Billy, I told you when he came yesterday - you wouldn't get up, so I shut the bedroom door.'

'What while you shagged him in that room?' His menacing stare made me realise I was about to be put through hell. My smile disappeared as I braced myself. He grabbed my hair, pulling me into the bathroom. I managed to grab the two door handles with my hands to stop him dragging me any further into the room. Screaming at him to get off me, I was dragged towards the hot water running in the bath. I didn't want to be scalded and my thoughts suddenly turned to being drowned. My life started to flash before me as I fought for my life. He was pulling at me and gripped his arm tightly around my neck. The door ripped away from the hinges still holding the handles, the door hit me in the face, cutting my lip and forehead. Dazed, my hold of the door loosened which gave him chance to get a stronger grip and drag me over to the sink. I wedged my hands on the edge of the sink, keeping my arms as rigid as possible afraid of what he was intending to do. He switched on the hot water tap of the hand basin. The water was scalding hot steam was causing a fog in the room. I fought to keep my head away from the tap as he pushed it from behind into the sink; if I had given up the fight, he would have scalded my face. I could feel hot drops of water as it splattered in the sink, spitting onto my face as I fought to resist the pressure bearing down on my head. He attempted to kick my legs from underneath me. Billy managed to remove my hands, which were clutching on for dear life to the sink. My head was forced down towards the water. Through my struggle I missed the water and smashed into the edge of the sink. Feeling faint, I could hear him calling me the usual derogatory names and swearing. I felt the punches begin to my ribs as he dragged me by my hair through the broken doorway into the bedroom. I couldn't speak as my mouth was full of blood from the split lip and the disorientation of the two collisions to my head. I tried to convey to him by pointing that his little girl was watching, but in his ferocious rage he pushed me on the bed. He knelt, straddling me, pinning me to the bed, the weight of his body securing me in place as his punches rained down onto my face until I was almost unconscious. I could hear my name being called: this made him let up with the cruel and viscous punching. He got off me. I realised Dave was shouting me, asking if I needed help. I slid off the bed barely conscious, landing in a heap on the floor at the foot of the bed. Writhing in pain, I couldn't answer Dave I hadn't the strength to breathe, let alone shout for help. At that point I saw a booted foot heading towards my face. I hadn't time to recoil into a ball for protection. I felt the direct impact as blood spurted out of my nose, splattering onto the bed covers and carpet. Then came two more kicks into my body, one to my groin and another to my tummy. Everything went black. Unable to move, I drifted in and out of consciousness all night. I saw a blurred vision of Lilly standing in her cot. She didn't cry. I strained to say,

'Lie down, sweetheart, go back to sleep, mummy's okay.'

I didn't know if she did as I said because all went dark again.

Each time I regained consciousness I tried to move, but the pain in my head was too intense. Blood was seeping down my face I hadn't a clue where it was coming from. Everywhere hurt and my eyes were closing with the bruising and swelling; at one point I felt I was dying. I remembered a few years earlier a woman who was beaten by her husband so badly he caused a blood clot to form. It killed her at a later date whilst she was sitting on a bar stool in a pub; I knew this woman. I felt for her and her family at the time; I felt now it was my turn, only it would be here on the bedroom floor. In a time of consciousness, I said the Lord's Prayer. I asked for forgiveness for whatever I had done to provoke these attacks. I asked Him to keep Lilly safe after I left this world. I drifted off into the darkness again; suddenly I felt peaceful and warm. I thought the Lord had come to fetch me.

I woke in the morning covered in blood, still unable to move. I didn't hear any sound from either Billy or Lilly. Our overnight guest had obviously been sent home. I strained to see if Lilly was in her cot: she had gone. Worried for her safety, I forced myself up by holding onto the bed clothes. The more I tried to get up, the more pain shot through my body and faintness took over. It didn't occur to me to realise I was still alive because finding my daughter was the most important thing. Covered in dried blood and wearing the previous night's blood-soaked clothes, I managed to crawl towards the door. Holding onto it, I pulled myself to my feet, hobbling to the stairs. My legs felt heavy and

I was doubled over with severe stomach pain. With one hand on the banister and the other holding my stomach trying to stem the pain, I slowly, foot by foot, step by step, made it down stairs to the living room. Still there was no sign of them. My heart was pounding - had he run away with her, leaving me for dead? I started to panic. Frantically I used the chairs to help me walk to the kitchen. I saw her pushchair, so I knew they couldn't be far away. I got to the window. I saw him sitting down at the chicken pen at the bottom of the garden. She looked safe sitting on Billy's knee and seemed happy with him. I used the sink for support, watching them for a few minutes - how could I take her away from her daddy who she loved so much? I managed to sit on the chair next to the table. I dared not look at the damage he had done this time, though I felt like he had broken my nose. The pain that consumed my body made it unbearable to sit, stand or move. I was conscious the shaking I was experiencing was due to shock and even then, I wasn't sure I was going to survive. The pain in my head continued to cause light-headedness. I could slightly see out of my left eye, but the right one was swollen closed; the vision in the left eye was blurred and it watered profusely. If I touched my face, the bruising and swelling was excruciatingly sore. The back of my head was still swelling and my nose and cheeks ached from the collision with his booted foot. It still hadn't occurred to me to be grateful for being alive. I knew it was going to frighten Lilly when she saw me. I heard the two of them chattering as they were coming up the garden path; Lilly's laughing was to be short-lived when she saw the state of me. As they neared the door, I put my head down to save her the fear of me. She walked over to me. I could feel her hand on my leg and heard her say,

'Poor mummy, hurt mummy,' in her sweet innocent voice.

I began to cry.

I patted her hand and Billy took her from me. He never commented on what he did. He didn't say sorry.

I was incapable of looking after myself, let alone Lilly. Billy made me soup but I was unable to eat it, so he took it away without a tantrum. He put Lilly to bed when she got tired and on returning downstairs he said the electricity was about to go off, so it would be better to go upstairs to save electricity and watch television in bed. I was too scared to disobey him. Being in bed with this monster was the last place I wanted to be: fearing this ogre of a man, I followed him upstairs. He was watching a programme on the bedroom television when I suddenly felt tears welling up in my eyes. I wasn't going to cry in front of him. I felt emotion welling up from deep within and I knew if I cried, I wouldn't stop. I feared how he would react. I knew another beating to my head could end my life. I got out of the bed. I felt his eyes watching me as I put on my dressing gown and, without a word between us, I slowly left the room and headed downstairs. I made my way through the dark towards the kitchen. There was a little armchair that had been given to me from the volunteer bureau when I first moved in my nice little house that had now become a house of horror. I sat for a few minutes, trying to gain enough courage to look at myself in the mirror. I had avoided them all day knowing this time it would be bad - had he disfigured me at last? He never allowed me out after a beating until the bruises had started to fade, but my skin was beginning to take on a permanent dark look especially around the eyes in particular, my left one. Eventually, feeling sick to the stomach, I summoned enough courage to stand and look into the mirror situated on the wall above the chair. I wasn't prepared for the person I saw looking back at me. The shock was something I have never forgotten. It took a few minutes for my mind to take in the horror I was seeing. My face had changed shape. The black and purple of deep bruising covered every inch of my skin - there wasn't one little space of natural colour left. Dried blood was smeared across my face and neck, which had swollen to twice its size. With one eye completely shut and the other only partially open, I was scanning this horrific face with tunnel vision. My nose, though not broken, looked as though it was bent to the right. I later found out the cartilage was fractured, a physical scar I still see every day. My lips were purple, cut and swollen and bruised, my blonde hair was dyed by the dried red blood. In shock, I fell to the chair. It was like looking at some graphic creature out of a horror movie. For a few minutes I couldn't move or take in the evidence before me. Never in my life would I have dreamt such cruelty would befall me. I lifted my legs and, with my feet under me, I curled into a ball. The flood gates were opened: I sobbed and sobbed. I cried loudly, uncontrollably. I was unrecognisable, even to myself. I don't know how long I was crying out loud, but all of a sudden I saw feet before me. Startled and feeling sick with fear, I looked up under my draping stained hair to see Billy at the doorway. He was looking sternly at me. Amidst my crying I said,

'What have you done to me?'

'Stop being melodramatic,' he turned to return upstairs.

I didn't move in fact I woke up in the morning still in the same place and position. Getting up to put the kettle on to make a drink, I caught a glimpse of my ugly face in the mirror. This time I inspected it. I felt the bumps on the top and back of my head that had swollen to almost twice its size. The body bruises, though bad and painful, paled into insignificance after I saw my reflection.

He didn't go out that day. I didn't go out for three weeks. I hid and saw no-one, not even Shirley our neighbour, who had taken to keeping out of our way. She was getting very frightened for my safety, especially after Anna had left. She had developed Obsessive Compulsive Behaviour. She had previously mentioned she could hear my screams and his beatings. I regularly heard her checking her doors were locked four or five times a night - she was terrified that Billy would go in her house to start on her. When he had gone out, she would regularly ring me to ask me to go and check her doors were locked. I did this for her, but still I could hear her pulling at the handles all night long.

Once my facial bruising was fading and the cuts began to heal, Billy announced we were going to his cousin Bob's the following day, so I had better clean myself up. It didn't matter to him that I was so very badly beaten. I began to think of excuses not to go but knew they wouldn't work. He had got used to everyone knowing he was a wife beater, so it didn't bother him anymore how I looked. I didn't matter to him. I was there to be a mother to our child when he allowed me. We left to catch the bus to go to Bob's house, which was a ten minute journey away. I tried to hide my face from the public: it was still slightly swollen and, though fading, the bruises were still shades of black, blue and purple. People on the bus gasped with shock as I walked on with Lilly, struggling to carry her and the folded pushchair which I placed in the closed space at the front of the bus. Putting Lilly in both arms near my face as a screen to shield my shame, I found the nearest empty seat. As Billy made his way down the bus, ignoring the comments made towards him by shocked passengers, he sat beside me and took Lilly. I knew not to try and stop him. I faced the front of the bus and spent the ten-minute journey looking out of the window, trying to ignore the public's whispers of disgust and sympathy, 'poor girl' and 'the monster' being just two comments that stuck in my mind. We arrived at his cousin's - I saw the look on their faces when they saw me, but still they acted as if nothing was wrong. The day panned out to be quite pleasant, especially for Lilly who was centre of attention for the family's three children. Sue asked me to come inside the house to help prepare lunch; it was a ploy of hers to get me alone.

'You're going to have to leave him - he's going to kill you one day,' she said, while she put chips in the oven to cook. She asked me to get out the plates, knowing that Billy wouldn't be far away.

'I know. I'm too scared. God knows what he will do if I took Lilly, because I'm not leaving without her.' I lowered my voice even more as I whispered 'he's already beaten Anna, my eight-year-old, and she is now with her dad.' I looked behind me and outside to make sure he wasn't listening. I had finally told someone he had beaten her. Somehow this eased some of the guilt I had been holding since the incident: it was like unloading the heaviness of my heart, to have someone to speak to. Billy came in at that point, giving me his knowing glare. I kept quiet for most of the time after that, until we left around teatime. Billy set off in his long strides down to the town. Still in pain in my groin and legs, I hobbled behind him as quick as I could. Finally I caught up on reaching the bus stop. I saw him checking the timetable for the next bus: without speaking, he started to walk in the direction of home. Trying to keep up I continued to follow him, the light-headedness and faint feeling still very much apparent. I was perspiring badly due to a combination of the summer heat and physical pain. We walked again for half a mile; my heart sank when I saw him turn into the car park of the local Miners' Welfare. Although I was appreciative of a rest for a while, I dreaded him getting even further drunk. Inside were some of his family, two aunts and three cousins, then I realised this was all planned in advance and would mean a long drinking session. They were playing a game of darts and they seemed happy to see him and Lilly. They were a very violent family and if he did this to me, then in their eyes I must have deserved it. So my facial features weren't mentioned or cared about. They wanted me to join in and make up the team for their darts contest. I flatly refused, to Billy's anger. I sat quietly with an orange juice, watching them laughing and playing their games of darts and dominos, hoping the day would pass quickly. I wasn't spoken to after my refusal to play darts. I watched Billy get slowly intoxicated, but instead of fearing his anger and sarcastic attitude, I somehow lost all fear of him. It was a strange feeling - all nerves had drained from me, whether because I was switching off for the inevitable beating that all his drunken states brought me, or whether I didn't care about me anymore, I wasn't sure. After a couple of hours of being ignored, he decided it was time to go home, he could then afford to go out later that night. I heard him say his goodbyes as I walked out of the door, ignoring them as they had me. Billy insisted on carrying Lilly, my request for him to put her in the pushchair being ignored. I followed behind him, concerned for her. As we got to the bus stop my concerns were realised. In his drunken state, he dropped Lilly. Her head smashed onto the pavement and though I ran to save her, I wasn't quick enough. She was screaming in pain and he raced to pick her up; a massive lump was appearing on the right side of her temple. I attempted to take her away from him; he gave her up easily as she pushed against him and tried to get her into my arms. Annoyance that she wanted me instead of him sent his eyes green. He had just dropped his daughter, injuring her, and I was still badly bruised, so what was he going to do? Beat me? I ignored his snide remarks and tended to Lilly. A bus pulled up and we boarded. I left the pushchair and went to sit down, comforting Lilly who had gone quiet in my arms. He struggled to collapse the pushchair and threw it in the appropriate space at the front of the bus, paid the driver and gave me a look that would turn anyone to stone. I didn't care. I ignored him. There were a lot of people on the bus and he had to sit away from me. I could feel his stare, which was broken by Lilly suddenly vomiting. She had gone into shock. We were almost home 202 was situated behind the next bus stop. I kept Lilly awake and was offered assistance by the lady sitting next to me, which I gratefully accepted. I urgently needed a doctor for my nineteen-month-old daughter. The bus stopped. I ran off the bus, thanking the lady for her concern. Leaving Billy to deal with the pushchair, I made my way home. Billy caught up with me as I was unlocking the door.

'She needs a doctor,' I said, as I carried Lilly in the living room. She was pale and continued her vomiting. I grabbed the phone, but as I dialled the number he took it off me and refused to let me ring.

'You stupid idiot drink's more important to you than anything else. Just fuck off to the pub.' I never swore, but this time he had to be spoken to in his own language. In shock that I dared to speak to him like this, he walked out of the room,

'No doctors, you deal with her.' The door slammed behind him.

Before he reached the gate at the top of the path, I was on the phone to the emergency services. They put me in touch with a doctor who said to keep her awake and he would be with us immediately. He was.

He examined her and agreed with me that she had concussion. He needed the information about how it happened. I told him the truth, not caring if the police were called. They weren't. He said to keep her warm and awake for at least two hours: in the event of her going limp I was to ring an ambulance immediately, giving the switchboard his name. I thanked him and I escorted him to the door where he asked:

'Are you alright my dear?' adding, 'you look like you have gone through the wars too.'

'Something like that,' I replied. 'I'm just worried for my baby'. I was too concerned with Lilly to answer more questions about me. He bid me goodnight, but before he went off into the night, he said:

'There are people to help you in this situation, they will protect you.'

I looked at him, not knowing what to say. I was tempted to say the word 'help' but knew I had Lilly to take care off. I had missed my chance yet again. Billy came home about an hour later around 10.30pm, concerned more about whether I had called a doctor than how his own daughter was. Ignoring him, I continued to cuddle and play with my Lilly. A few days later I realised why he fled when he knew I would call a doctor, it was because there would now be a record of an injury caused by him - and the fact that I was still quite badly bruised and would be seen by the doctor, a credible witness. Like the coward he was, he ran out of the way. A week after this incident I was vacuuming upstairs in my bedroom, popping downstairs to fetch the polish and a duster. I walked into the living room unexpectedly and what I saw infuriated me. Lilly had been walking around in her nappy and shorts it was a very hot day. Still unsteady on her feet, she started to scream. On her chest was a freshly made burn.

'She just walked into my fag,' he shouted, looking guilty. 'It was an accident.'

'What the hell you doing with a fag near her anyway?' I roared at him while I picked her up and used a cold wet tea towel to ease her pain. He darted upstairs out of my way. Calming her down, I rocked her to sleep and laid her safely on her blankets on the floor. I went upstairs to collect the hoover. Billy was in bed: it was 3 o'clock in the afternoon. I picked up the hoover, accidently hitting the on-switch. He jumped up so quickly, he obviously was not asleep. I felt his hands around my neck as he slammed me into the corner of the bedroom wall. I must have blacked out because the next thing I knew he was yelling at me,

'Now fetch your brothers.'

As I came round and tried to stand up, my legs went to jelly and I collapsed again. Dazed I said,

'You'd be scared if I did.' This was not my usual answer of 'I wouldn't give you the satisfaction.'

This made him even more furious and he grabbed me again, whisking me into the air and smashing me once again into the wall. I felt a sharp pain in my head as he squeezed my throat.

I gasped for air and made a funny gurgling sound as my feet struggled to find the floor. He wouldn't let go of me. It all went black as I saw Lilly and Anna in my mind's eye. I don't know how long I was unconscious in a heap on the floor, except to say when I opened my eyes I could see panic in his. I think he thought he had finally taken my life. When he saw me looking at him, he strode over me and ran downstairs and out of the door at the bottom of the stairs. He arrived home later, sober. We didn't speak. Two weeks later he burnt Lilly again, this time on her forearm - this caused a big argument, but he didn't attack me this time. I knew that because Lilly was the only way to get to me now, he would continue to hurt her in order to hurt me. He hated me more than he loved her. In all she was burnt three times; the third one I didn't see until she was bathed the next morning, it was on her shoulder. I spoke to him about it and got a beating to keep my mouth shut. I had virtually stopped eating altogether and my body was bruised flesh over bones, but I was determined to survive this life and be with both of my daughters. It was the only thing that kept me focused something to stay alive for.

A Dash for Freedom

It was a usual Friday in September. Billy got up and had a bath and shave; his aftershave smelt cheap and nasty. He put on clean clothes and was in a good mood. It was benefit week. He had a cup of tea and a couple of cigarettes. As he walked out the door to cash his benefit cheque, he ordered me to,

'Be in the club at 1 o'clock.'

Whether I wanted to be or not wasn't my choice. The heaviness of the house's atmosphere lifted, if only for a short while, when he had gone out. When we were ready, with Lilly in her pushchair, I walked slowly, pushing her up the road. For around a month after the beating over the cigarette burns on Lilly, his violence stopped, although his verbal abuse continued. As we got closer to the park, Lilly got excited: it was very rare she went to play on the swings. I was virtually under house arrest and Billy never took her out, other than to his family's house. I promised her if she was good we would take her later. I just had to convince Billy to take us otherwise there wouldn't be any chance of going. I walked into the club, where he was waiting for us. Everyone said 'hello' but they were very wary of saying much more to me, in case of causing problems. I quietly replied and took my place next to Billy, who was playing cards with the men, losing the benefit money as usual.

'What took you so long?' He asked, even though it was just one o'clock. He was still quite sober at that point.

'We had a bath.' I didn't elaborate on the slow walk up. 'Lilly wanted to go to the park but I said you were waiting for us and we might take her after we leave.' He nodded in approval, so I knew he wasn't in a bad mood. I tried to be good so as not to spoil the trip to the park for Lilly. He said we needed shopping and electricity, so he gave me some money folded up, saying,

'Hang on to that before these bastards win it from me,'

causing everyone to laugh. He thought he was a funny, well-liked man but the thing was they were trying to pacify him, knowing that upsetting him meant I got beaten. I just half smiled and continued to talk to Lilly, as she was playing and chattering as small toddlers do. Billy won a few hands of cards, which put him in an even better mood. We were there for a few hours, which was usual for a payday. I was very careful not to speak to anyone I shouldn't, or do anything to change his unusually friendly mood. Around 4pm I saw him put the money he had on the table into his pocket; he looked at me and said politely,

'Come on then, swings for us,' with a smile that I hadn't seen for over a year and a half. He took hold of Lilly's hand and started walking with her. I said my 'goodbyes' with a rare smile, because he had meant what he said and hadn't let Lilly down. I followed behind him with the pushchair. He was happily chatting to Lilly, who was excitedly responding, enjoying the nice atmosphere between her parents. We reached the park and I knew not to take things for granted: I knew he could change moods on the flip of a coin, but he seemed quite genuinely pleasant - maybe he had decided to change towards us. I started relaxing, knowing I had the shopping money probably only £20, but at least it was something and I could do wonders with £20. He put Lilly on the slide and I caught her; her giggles made us laugh. It was strange to hear Billy laughing because he hadn't happily laughed for two years. We swapped roles and he caught her, which made her laugh more, then she ran over to the huge cement pipes laid out in a maze. Lilly was small enough to run inside them, giggling and shouting with excitement, her echo adding to her fun. Coming out of the other end of the pipes, she ran to the swings. Lifting her inside the enclosed baby swing, Billy walked behind her to push her. He seemed to be enjoying himself and this was the first time we had done something together, other than going to his family or the pub/club, since we met. I stepped to the side of the swinging toddler, who was shouting,

'More, daddy!' her laughter increased.

She went higher and higher, each time shouting for more. I sat on a swing at the end of the row, watching and smiling at their interaction. He walked to the front of her and looked at me. I smiled at him. I could see him thinking as he was slowing down Lilly's swing.

'You fucking whore,' he growled, turning back to Lilly and getting her out of the swing. The laughing stopped. Lilly obviously recognised the change of tone in his voice. I looked at him as he continued,

'You're nothing but a slag. God, what am I thinking letting you be a mam to my child?'

I began to tremble. Getting off the swing, I saw his eyes change to bright green. I knew what was going to happen to me. In my fear, I panicked. I ran one way, then another; terrified. I couldn't think straight. I ran to Lilly but he wouldn't let me near her, he picked her up, holding her tightly to him and leering at me.

'Yes, you better run you bitch.'

I didn't know where to run or who to run to. I could see the hatred in his face. I knew I was in for trouble: maybe this was the day I was waiting for, the day it all ended. I ran again to take Lilly off him, but his arm stretched out preventing me, he wouldn't let me take her. The panic was getting worse and terror began to fill the pit of my stomach. I hadn't done anything or said anything wrong. He put Lilly in the pushchair, all the time growling derogatory names at me, 'useless bitch, fucking whore, fat cow, and ugly slag' where just a few and then he started shouting I was a 'murdering baby killer' (he was referring to Thomas). I was running around, unsure how to get away, but couldn't because he had Lilly it was pure torment. Lilly's laughter had turned to crying as she sensed my fear and heard his voice turn to the 'evil one before mummy gets hurt'. Once she was strapped into the pushchair, I thought about running back to the club for safety. I set off in that direction but then realised no-one in there would protect me. I turned to run towards his parents' house, but then stopped; I knew they were scared of him and I wouldn't be safe. My parent's, no, I couldn't take this trouble to their door. I must have looked like a scared rabbit fleeing a chasing dog, only I wasn't getting anywhere. I heard him say,

'I'm taking her to my mam's. You go home I will meet you there in a bit. Get some clothes packed we can't go on like this.'

I knew he would leave her with his family while he came to 202. I thought at least she wouldn't see him kill me. That's why he was taking her to his mum's. I knew my time had finally come. I ran out of the park gate and down the main road to 202. I went immediately upstairs, clutching two plastic carrier bags. I grabbed some of Lilly's clothes and nappies - anything I could get my hands on in the short time I had. I knew he would soon be there. This was it: one way or another, I was out of there. I just had to 'stay strong'. Grabbing the other carrier bag, I placed some of my personal things, underwear and a couple of tops inside. I ran back downstairs, missing the last two steps and falling but there was no time for pain. I got up and ran into the kitchen where her potty was kept; she was just being toilet-trained. I ran back upstairs and placed the potty in the bag on top of my clothes, knowing he would stop me taking her clothes but let me take mine. I knew how he worked. Her clothes were more important: I could go without, but Lilly couldn't. I put on an extra layer of clothes and a thick pullover to cover my arms. I knew either way it was going to hurt. I looked around the room and removed anything to hand he could use to injure me. I removed the knives from the kitchen drawer, putting them behind the toilet outside. All the time, I was thinking that he would probably strangle me anyway. Secure in my mind I had done all I could to help my survival I sat by the window in the hope of seeing his mood as he came towards the gate. My neighbour Shirley was moving out that day: she had had enough of listening to the violence and living in fear. She had put herself into a residential care home. Her kitchen door was open, with her son John standing inside the door: he had seen the state of my panic as he watched me run down the path, terrified. He had asked if I was okay. I couldn't answer him, though he knew how scared of Billy I was through his conversations with his mother. I thought while the door was open he would help if he heard screams. I heard the wheels of the pushchair nearing the gate. I stood up and swiftly moved nearer the window, looking for Billy's facial expression. I was going to fight him if I had to, believing I would be fighting for my life. I was constantly shaking - he saw this when he walked in. He took Lilly out of her pushchair and she came running to me. I picked her up, but he snatched her off me. I went into the kitchen to check the door was still open. It wasn't so I opened it quietly, fearing he would hear me. I placed the pushchair in the front of the door to enable a quick getaway if necessary. All I knew was I wasn't going anywhere without my baby - he would have to kill me first. John saw what I was doing from the door opposite, watching events unfolding. I hoped he would help if things got too bad; after all men who hit women rarely hit men. I returned to the living room where he was sitting with Lilly on his knee. I needed him to start while John was standing outside, not like he usually did after some tormenting first. I said,

'I've packed some things like you said. You're right we can't go on like this.' I felt sick, as I had to push him to either attack me or let me get out of there.

'Where are they?'

'I've left them upstairs,' I said, hoping he meant what he said and was going to let us go.

'Fetch them.'

'If I do that you will get angry and you will kill me,' I shook uncontrollably as I spoke.

'I said fetch them,' Billy's voice bellowing so loud John must have heard.

I kept my eyes on him until I reached the stairs door. I didn't want him to follow me. I managed to get upstairs unharmed. I picked up the bags and returned to the living room, in spite of my legs refusing to move. It was sheer willpower. I knew the sight of the bags would cause him to attack me. He abruptly stood up, dropping Lilly to the floor. She didn't cry; she just watched with fear in her eyes. Within seconds my head banged into the corner of the wall. I was ready for his attack and found that tensing my neck prevented him crushing my throat so easily. I looked past him to see Lilly as she ran as fast as her little legs could carry her. She grabbed hold of his pullover with her tiny hands, clung on to him and started to pull at his pullover in her attempts to stop what he was doing to me.

'No daddy, no daddy, no daddy, no,' she was shouting as loud as she could.

He couldn't hear her; he was in such a rage. I let go of his hand which was throttling me, his grip getting tighter around my neck. I managed to somehow croak out the words,

'Look, Billy, look - Lilly.' I pointed to her.

He felt the tugging on his clothes. Still hanging on to my throat, he turned to see his baby daughter trying to save her mummy's life. He let go. I was dizzy from the bang on the head. I fell to the floor. My legs were like two sticks of limp celery, but I found the strength from somewhere to get back to my feet as he shouted,

'Get out … Take her to my mam's.'

That was it. That was my chance. I fought my failing body to stay on my feet. I picked her up and placed her in the pushchair. I threw my pullover off to enable me to run faster. John saw what I was doing and came nearer to the centre of our joint path. I looked at him frantically, then I ran back to pick up the bags containing the clothes.

'Leave them,' he yelled, 'take yours leave hers here. I'll bring them up later.'

I left the one containing the potty, grabbing the other bag as quickly as I could. I had fooled him. Desperate to get out, I started to take Lilly sitting in the pushchair down the kitchen steps, all the time hoping he wouldn't order me to stop. John moved forward to get the bottom of the pushchair to aid my escape. He said,

'Run gal. Run for your bloody life. If he comes out, I'll stop him.'

In my frantic dash for freedom, I shouted,

'Goodbye, Shirley. I'm sorry.' I negotiated the two concrete steps leading up to the small green council gate. The gate slammed shut behind me. I heard the clattering of metal as the latch grabbed the catch.

8.45a.m 21st September

Lilly woke with her little smile beaming across her face when she saw me sitting by the window. I noticed it was a bright sunny day outside: I had been so deep in my thoughts of horror that I missed the morning creeping upon us. Lilly was by now standing up on mum's bed with her arms stretched open to be picked up, wobbling in her un-steadiness to reach me. I put all thoughts of the past to the back of my mind, as I whisked her up into my arms and hugged her.

'Good morning, sweetheart,' I said.

Her smile blew away any emotional distress my recollections over the night had resurrected. We made our way downstairs in search of breakfast cereal. Dad was downstairs and sitting at the table drinking his tea.

'I heard you had a visitor last night,' he said, putting his cup down.

'Yes, it was frightening for mum and her guests. I knew he would come, he isn't about to let me take Lilly away from him without a fight. The thing is he fights dirty, he smashed milk bottles and threatened mum with them.'

'Yes, your mother told me, but I'm sure she seen him off,' he said with a slight laugh.

I still didn't think dad realised the violence Billy was capable of.

Nothing more was said on the subject. Mum entered the kitchen and said to dad that he was to accompany me up to 202 to fetch some clothes and essentials; she instantly saw the look of terror on my face.

'Leave Lilly here,' she said which calmed me. 'Ring the police and they will accompany you.'

I did as she advised: the police were aware of the previous night's callout and the history of the violence, and after mum had discussed it with them, they were only too happy to meet me at 202. We arranged it for 10am. Although I didn't relish the idea of facing him, I knew it would be much easier if it was before he had been drinking. After what he had put me through over the last two years, I didn't feel dad or the policeman were really capable of protecting me against him. I kissed Lilly goodbye and said for her to be good for her mamma. We left for the two mile journey up the road. My fear returned as we neared 202 and seeing the little green gate caused my mouth to dry up as I tried to keep my nerves in check. Even the sight of the police car

awaiting our arrival did nothing to ease my fear. My legs began
to shake. I couldn't believe I was going to face this monster. As
we walked to the gate, the policeman began walking up the path
towards me.

'I have had a word with him and he will let you get your
things,' he said.

'Where are you going?' I asked him frantically.

'I'll be in my car if you need me to intervene.' He looked
surprised I even asked.

'How are you going to protect me sitting in your car? Oh no,
no you're not,' I insisted grabbing hold of his arm, 'I'm not going
in there without your assistance he's a lunatic he will kill me.'

The policeman looked into my eyes: he could see how
fearful I was, even with dad there to help protect me. He felt the
uncontrollable shaking of my hand as it stuck like glue to his arm.

'Alright, don't worry, you will be safe, but if you need me with
you I'm happy to come and assist.'

Did no-one comprehend the severity of this man's evilness?
As we neared the kitchen door, I pushed the policeman in front
of me and with dad behind him I stayed in the rear, trembling
like a leaf in the wind. The policeman stepped to one side as he
reached the door.

'Go in - there is no way I am entering that house first,' I said
firmly.

Looking at me pitifully, he realised how afraid of Billy I was.
From that moment the policeman took control of the situation
and entered the house. Dad followed him with me cautiously
tailing behind. I saw Billy sitting in the chair near the window.
His stare was cold as his eyes fixed on me standing in the
doorway of the living room. I stepped back, hiding myself in
my protector's shadow until my escorts went before me to make
it safe to pass him on the way upstairs to collect my belongings.

'Where is she?' Billy demanded to know.

Ignoring him, I nervously crept through the room heading
for the stairs door, sticking as close to the wall as possible. I
could see his face had been beaten; all shades of bruising were
beginning to appear down his right cheek. He saw me looking at
them, but I was too afraid to say anything because I didn't want

to antagonize him. As I neared the stairs door, he attempted to stand.

'Sit down,' dad demanded, 'and stay where you are.' Dad's voice was powerful and assured. Dad moved closer to him and stood before him, preventing him getting up from the chair. Billy for once looked so small with a man hovering over him. Billy looked towards the policeman.

'Do as you are told.' The stern face of the constable showed he realised the extent of my fear and wanted to quell any friction between Billy and dad. He moved to the near side of the chair, encasing Billy with only the window to his left. I passed unharmed while a cold shiver travelled down my spine. I tried to ignore the feeling of sickness in the pit of my stomach and the tremble of fear that ran through every inch of my body. I took a deep breath and made my way upstairs to the bedroom. Opening the black bin liner mum had given to me; I filled it with my clothes and personal belongings. I filled another with Lilly's things and then headed for the laundry basket, collecting all our clothes that were awaiting washing, knowing I could do them at mums. It wasn't a very nice feeling, leaving my home, and I began to well up with tears as I looked around for anything that I may have left behind. I heard a voice sternly shout,

'Sit down.' It made me jump in anticipation. Billy had obviously attempted to follow me but was prevented and was being closely guarded. This made me quicken up knowing how nasty he was, I still wasn't confident that he wouldn't get up the stairs to attack me. I threw the three bags of clothes down the stairs. I didn't feel capable of carrying them I was too weak. Flashes in my mind came of the last time I took the two carrier bags downstairs and this instilled yet more fear in me. With one last look at the damage done to the bedroom where most of the attacks had occurred, I slowly headed downstairs. Reaching the bottom, I picked up the bags and looked to see if Billy was still guarded before I entered the room. He was staring out of the window. I could sense he was furious, and though protected, I was still terrified. I began to walk slowly through the room; I saw the bag containing the potty was still by the wall. Dad took the bags off me while the policeman stood watching Billy,

'Is that it?' dad asked.

'No, just some toys for Lilly - they're in the kitchen cupboard.'

I reached down to pick up the bag by the wall. I felt dizzy and had to steady myself by holding onto the wall. The pressure filling my head hurt. I waited for my mind to become clear then continued into the kitchen to Lilly's toys which had been put away and tidied; picking up some of her favourite dolls and books, I saw the pullover on the chair where it had landed in my need to escape. Picking it up, I headed for the door, taking the key out of the keyhole and placing it in my pocket. I didn't look back at the policeman as I said,

'That's it, I'm ready.' Then I heard Billy shout,

'You have all the money, I need some.'

Immediately dad's voice intervened,

'Don't you give him anything he will only drink it and come causing trouble.' I didn't acknowledge his request for money

'This is my officer number. If you have any further problems with him, ring and ask for me. It is best to stick with one officer as they get to know the case and the people involved. I will ring you occasionally to see if things are okay, but you must get a court order to get him out of your house and I advise you now, you need a good solicitor in respect of your daughter.'

I thanked him for his help, and as he got into his car wishing me luck, he turned to dad and told him to take care of me. The officer became invaluable in future crises of Billy's persistent drunken visits to my house. Of which there were to be many.

Being with my parents over the weekend enabled me to think clearly about Lilly's and my future. It was nice to have some peace and though sleeping at night was impossible listening for Billy's drunken visits, I managed an hour or so during the day when mum insisted I rested upstairs while she watched Lilly. She had realised that I hadn't had much rest over the last few years and did all she could to enable me to get stronger. I decided to seek a solicitor as soon as possible and the following Monday I ventured out, leaving Lilly safely with mum, to find some professional help. I was fortunate to see someone immediately at an office at the top of the street near the town centre. He was a young man, tall and thin, and seemed very understanding. I told him the details of what had been happening in my relationship with Billy. It was hard for me to tell him the extent of Billy's brutality towards myself and my daughters, pinpointing the fact that he had beaten Anna so badly she had to go to her dad's for safety, and the cigarette burns on Lilly's body. Taking notes of what I was conveying to him, he declared:

'I will get this typed up and apply for an injunction to keep him away from you and your children; this should keep you safe. I will also take steps to return your house to you; though this will mean you appearing in court for the injunction and to re-take possession. Although it's in your name and a local authority house, he has officially lived there, so we have to do it legally. Are you alright to stay at your parents' as this could take up to three months?'

'Yes that's not a problem I just want him to stay away from my parents' house.'

'The injunction will prevent him from coming within a certain distance of you, which will be decided by the judge. I will get on to it today and will write to you soon.'

Thanking him for his help, I left his office feeling I was finally taking control of my life, and although it would be a slow process, at least the first stage was under way. The feeling of being a victim had started to subside (though that feeling didn't last for long). Feeling proud I had started to make steps to rebuild my life, I asked dad to run me to the next town to the benefits office. I couldn't expect my parents to support Lilly and I so I had to inform them what had happened and make a claim for benefit. Dad was happy to take me everywhere to ensure my safety. I decided to take Lilly with us on this journey, to give mum a break. We reached the social security office and were directed to the fresh claims department upstairs. I was horrified to see Billy in the waiting room. I stood on the top step of the stairs; my feet froze to the ground. Dad eased me in the doors, reassuring me he wouldn't allow him to hurt me. Again I came face-to-face with my abuser.

'Daddy! Daddy!' The joy in Lilly's voice at seeing her father was obvious as she ran towards him.

The swellings on his face had doubled in size since I last saw him two mornings previously. The cuts and abrasions looked sorely red and his eye appeared partially closed. I was next in line to see the advisor, so I had to sit near him.

'Poor daddy, bruised like mummy,' Lilly stated in her sweet innocent voice.

'What happened to you?' I asked, as I took the seat next but one to him. I knew he couldn't start any trouble in there it was a government building and he would be immediately arrested. Dad sat opposite us and never took his eyes off him.

'The bastards laid me out on Friday night,' he said in a sorrowful voice in the hope of getting a sympathetic response. 'Then I was grabbed off the settee by our Dave. Before I could stop him, he had dragged me out into the garden and battered me.' I tried to hide the smugness I was feeling at the fact he had received a little of what he had dished out to me. He continued as he cuddled Lilly on his knee, 'I woke up about 2am: none of the neighbours came to help or wake me up. Dave just left me there.'

'We have no neighbours Billy they all left after they couldn't stand the noise of your violence, or hadn't you noticed?' My sarcasm far outweighed any smugness I felt. 'It hurts, doesn't it Billy?'

There was no response to my statement as he realised any sympathy he was trying to coax from me was futile. Before any further exchange of words, he was called in for his interview. I could hear him telling her that I had left him, taking the baby with me and I had taken all the money and he hadn't any. I also heard her say to him that because the money was in his name, he would have to wait for his next payment when it was due in eleven days, but it would be reduced to a single person's rate. I sighed with relief, knowing he would be struggling to buy beer for two weeks. As my name was called, I was directed to the booth next to him. I began to tell the male interviewer the circumstances that had bought me there. I explained Billy was in the next booth also being interviewed. The kind gentleman, concerned for my safety, directed me to a door marked interview room 2. I was greeted by him opening the door from the inside.

'You can be safe in here and tell me exactly what's been happening without fear. Do you have anyone with you?' he asked in a concerned manner.

'Yes my dad's out there with our daughter, Lilly.'

'Would you like me to fetch them in here for you?'

'No, dad will look after Lilly. Billy doesn't stand up to men - he only beats women.'

He looked sympathetic and we began the interview. I told him I had £60 out of the benefit cheque. He looked at me and the state I was in and said,

'That was the cheque Mr Burnshaw received last Friday morning?' I nodded in agreement, 'Well, we don't need to know that looking at you, I think you will need that until your claim goes through.'

I wasn't used to anyone being nice to me and this bought a lump to my throat and tears to my eyes.

'I will rush your claim through, Mrs Burnshaw.'

'We weren't married can you change it to my maiden name please, Ms Preston?'

'Certainly Ms Preston, I think that might be a good idea. What about Lilly - have you thought about changing hers: after all, you aren't married to him, are you?'

'No,' I answered. 'I have only been divorced from Mark, Anna's father, a few months. I'm thankful for that or I might have made an even bigger mistake early in our relationship.'

'Where is Anna? That's your 8-year-old, isn't it?' he asked while checking my file.

'She is living with her father.' I lowered my head in shame as I continued. 'Billy beat her so violently she had to go to her dad's for safety.' Lifting my eyes, I saw the intense look of disgust in his eyes.

He said that they would rush the claim through because of special circumstances. He asked if I had a photograph of Billy for the Child Support Agency as they would be claiming money off him to help support Lilly.

'I don't want money off him. I don't want him having anything to do with us at all. If he supports Lilly, he will think he has a claim to her and I need to fight for him to leave her alone, he is violent to her too. It means he will still be in our lives. Please don't do this. I will get work once I'm on my feet. I will support her', I begged.

He explained it was the law. He saw the fear in my eyes.

'You really are terrified of him, aren't you?'

I nodded. He thought for a few seconds and then said gently,

'Don't worry, in some special cases, and it seems your case is we can decide that if it is going to cause detriment to you or your child, we can stop any legal claim for maintenance support. Is this what you would like to do?'

'Yes,' I insisted.

'You ought to get a solicitor, Jeannette. He sounds a vile man.'

I slightly smiled and assured him it was already in hand. He closed the file and sat back in his chair and said,

'I hope you don't think all men are like that, because we are not. Right, I'll get your money pushed through quickly. It will be sent to your parents' address. Please stay away from him Ms Preston - you deserve better. Please just sit there for a minute while I check he has left the building; there is no need to put your-self in danger.'

Within a few minutes he returned and escorted me into the waiting area to dad and Lilly. At the door was a burly security guard who walked down the steps before us. As we reached the door to the street, he took one look outside and smiled saying, 'I think you're safe now.'

I remember thinking 'I wish'.

On returning home to mum's, I gave her the £60 for our food with a view to a regular amount every week once the benefit came through. She refused it saying,

'We will go out tomorrow. I think you need that money to get yourself some new clothes and I will buy Lilly some new things.'

Again, I fought back tears - it was difficult to cope with people helping or being nice to me. It was alien to me, though it was very much appreciated.

The following Tuesday, eight days after my first interview, I was on my way to the solicitor's office to sign forms for the proceeding to start against Billy; at the solicitor's request to see me. To my surprise, the solicitor was standing a few yards away from his office.

'Hello,' he said, 'I'm sorry, but I can't take your case.'

He handed to me all the documents containing my statements that I had previously told him the week before.

'Sorry,' he said, and turned and walked away.

I stood flabbergasted, not knowing what to do or say. He gave no explanation or excuses. I turned around and walked back down the road to mum's. I was stunned. Mum was so angry when I told her what had happened that she rang her solicitors' firm in the town and made me an appointment. I was to go up that afternoon.

Entering the office of mum's solicitors, I felt my confidence had taken a drop after the earlier performance by the man, who had so off handily rejected my case. The receptionist in this establishment was certainly more professional. Being asked to be seated, I noticed a small red-headed woman as she came rushing into the reception area, all of a flutter.

'Ms Preston?' Her smile was bright as her hair, which made me smile. 'Please come this way.' I followed her into a small room at the end of a corridor, it had freshly painted walls and a bunch of fresh cut flowers decorated her desk, which looked very large with the small, pleasant lady sitting in the chair behind it. 'Now then,' she looked at me with friendly eyes, 'I hear you have been having a little difficulty with your previous solicitor -our receptionist explained a little of what happened. Could you tell me yourself what actually happened?'

I could see her smile change as I explained the series of events with the rude and incompetent man I had put my trust into over a week ago. I noticed her head begin to slightly shake in disapproval as she listened intently to my experience.

'Please accept my apologies on behalf of our profession. I assure you this is not normal practice.' Her apology was genuinely meant and I began to relax, thinking that maybe I was better to be in the hands of a more established firm. I handed her the file that I had been given and had perused before attending this appointment. Everything I had conveyed to him had been professionally noted, which helped the lady instantly come to grips with my problems.

'I myself do not actually specialise in domestic affairs, especially ones of such magnitude. You certainly have reason to be worried about your ex-partner, especially in connection to your daughter Lilly. Before you arrived I had a chat to one of our associates, explaining what I had been informed about your case. I feel she is the person that would make a big difference to your case. The thing is her office is in the city centre, would that be a problem for you?' I indicated it wouldn't. 'Good, because reading your file I feel you are going to need the best: this Billy seems a force to be reckoned with, but I must admit, Mrs Radford is the best in the country and this is her area of expertise.' While she spoke, she dialled a number on her telephone and began to talk to a lady I heard her call Rebecca. I couldn't have appreciated at the time how important Rebecca would become in my life.

Protecting Lilly

It was a Thursday in November when the meeting took place with Rebecca Radford, a tall, elegant lady. She was very friendly and I took an instant liking to her: she made me feel at ease with the first handshake.

'Please take a seat. I have heard what the previous solicitor did, let me assure you we are not all like that and I apologise on behalf of my profession. Now, I have read your file. If I take on your case, you might have to come to the city to see me at my office in the future. I have a very heavy workload, but will try as much as possible to come here but I'm in court most of the time. So you coming to my office in the city, would that be a problem?'

I assured her it wouldn't.

'I feel greatly for your treatment at the hands of this man, Billy. Do you wish to prosecute him at all for personal damages?'

'No, I just want my council house back, and to be protected from him. He wants to see Lilly, but I fear for her safety,' I explained.

'Yes, I can well understand your reasoning in this matter. Well I am happy to take your case on - on condition you tell me every step of the way, the truth. I don't want any surprises when we end up in court,' her manner was friendly but serious.

I made and stuck to my promise. She gave me another appointment, so we could go over the information carefully after she had studied my statements. I was told not to let Lilly go to Billy for the foreseeable future. That suited me fine. I left her office feeling like the fight had begun - only this time I was in control.

My friends had gradually heard of my escape and return home to my parents and were slowly contacting me. Although I was too afraid to go to see them, it was nice to know they were thinking of me. I knew this was going to be a long battle. Billy wouldn't give up, not because he wanted to see Lilly, but because it was another way of controlling my life. Around a couple of weeks later, I received a letter from his solicitor demanding I let him see Lilly. I sent it to Mrs Radford. A court date was arranged and he was granted an interim order to see her. It didn't seem to matter what I told them; they would take no notice, as I hadn't any witnesses to corroborate his violence to either myself or Lilly: it was his word against mine. They did, however, make a stipulation that he refrained from drinking any alcohol while he had access and that the visit should take place at his mother's home. I reluctantly agreed to the terms, on the advice of Mrs Radford.

I had been at my parents' for around three weeks. One particular night I had gone to bed early, feeling fatigued through stress and mental exhaustion. If things were getting to me I would cry in private, as the horrific life I had endured engulfed me from time to time. Though my parents never said, 'I told you so' I still felt ashamed of my life and I deeply regretted letting my parents down. Lying awake, I heard mum go to her room around 11.30pm. Dad passed my door, going into my old bedroom, around an hour later. I must have eventually dozed off to sleep. I was startled as I woke to see blue lights flashing through the bedroom window. Instinctively I thought 'Billy'. I got up and ran to the window to find mum being put in an ambulance. My eyes scanned for police cars and I worried I had been asleep and missed him coming down and assaulting mum. I put on my dressing gown and ran downstairs.

'What's happening, what's wrong with mum?' I frantically asked dad, who was at the gate; he turned to walk into the house as the doors of the ambulance closed. With flashing lights and siren, it drove off.

Flashing lights and siren, it drove off at speed.

'Mum's very poorly, she's had an angina attack.' He saw my worried expression and explained what it meant. After a talk with dad I returned upstairs to Lilly, who was sleeping soundly. I began to feel guilty and thought maybe the ordeal with Billy had caused this heart condition through threats and worry. It was to be guilt-ridden sleepless nights until she came home. Mum wasn't allowed home for over a week; she had not been taking her medication for her diabetes, which resulted in problems causing the angina attack. During her absence, for reasons of his own, dad left.

Mum was very weak after her illness and distraught about dad leaving. I dealt with her grief, my own fears and the impending court case over Lilly; it was all taking its toll on my own health. It was a pleasure to repay the kindness to mum, for her protection and love she had shown me, but nevertheless it was hard work while I was still coping with the problems concerning Billy. She did eventually get stronger and we recovered our ordeals together. Soon we were talking about having Anna come to visit. She had her regular visits to my parents stopped by her daddy once he realised I was there, in order for me to gain control of my life and not to add any more pressure onto me. Mum suggested it would be better for her to talk to Mark and ask him to bring her to visit. I was both excited and nervous as they walked in the gate on that first Sunday morning visit. In her excitement Anna ran down the street and pushed open the unlocked gate, her face beaming a smile so bright it lit my world up. Her hug was huge and tight as she embraced me. It was a special moment in time. Just as eager to hug her sister, tears of joy filled her eyes as she ran to Lilly shouting 'bye' to her daddy, she sat on the floor. My two children played together with ease as if they had never been parted.

'I am pleased you got away from him - he was slowly killing you,' Mark said to me as he held me in his arms.

'Thank you for forgiving me for what happened to Anna. I'm deeply sorry and ashamed,'

'It's his shame, Jeannette, not yours,' he said, as he released me from his arms. That was the last hug he ever gave me and it sealed his forgiveness and friendship.

'I will fetch her around 7pm - is that okay?'

'Thank you,' I mouthed as my emotions prevented my words to be spoken; as he headed through the gate the smile between us said a thousand words.

I felt mum's arms around me as she softly comforted me, realising the past few years had been very hard on me.

I felt mum place her arms around me; she softly comforted me, realising the past few years had been very hard on her only daughter.

'Stay strong, you're doing really well and things will pick up. You have your girls in there playing and Anna's back in your life. Come on, Jeannie, you've come so far.' Her words were heartfelt and supportive. Taking in a deep breath, I composed myself and returned to my children. One of the concerns both mum and I had was Lilly's behaviour with her dolls. There were times she hid behind the settee to play with her dolls and we both heard her banging into the back of the settee. I peered behind to see what she was doing and was shocked to see her hitting her doll with a closed fist, over and over again.

'No, Lilly,' I said, trying not to seem angry. I pulled the settee out to enable me to sit beside her. 'Lilly sweetie, don't hurt dolly like that you will hurt her, like this, Look.' I took her doll and hugged and rocked it in my arms, giving it a kiss, 'like mummy does to you, sweetheart, dolly will like that.' I handed her back her doll, Lilly smiled and copied my actions. The look of confusion at what I had just said made me realise that, though she may have not understood the beatings Billy had inflicted on me, she thought it was a natural form of behaviour. I was devastated, but with time and patience mum, Anna and I changed her perception of love.

During the following October half-term holidays from school, Mark had asked if I would like Anna to come to stay. I was overjoyed at the thought of us all being together for a whole week. Mum was happy with the idea and we spent a lovely time as a family. The dreaded Sunday arrived and we solemnly packed Anna's belongings into her bag ready for her return to her daddy's. It had been a week which had built my confidence to become a good mum once more. Knowing Anna loved and missed me as much as I did her, gave me the lift I needed to regain control of my life and to 'stay strong' to fight Billy for full custody of Lilly. We sat after we had eaten Sunday lunch but everyone was subdued, knowing our funny little girl was again leaving us.

I had seen her character shine through in this week and my heart was breaking at the thought of our separation again, even though it was only for a week until her next visit.

'I don't want to go home, mummy. I want to stay here with you and Lilly and mamma.' Anna's eyes filled with tears at the thought of leaving us. There was a stunned silence - the little girl had the guts to say what we were all feeling.

'Ring Mark,' mum said, as she looked at me.

'Do you think he will, mum?'

'You won't know if you don't ask him,' she replied full of optimism.

I didn't need telling twice. I rose from the table, feeling all eyes on my back. I dialled Mark's parents' home number. I knew he would be there having lunch after his Sunday pint. My mouth felt dry with nerves. I forced the words out, as Mark's mum answered the telephone.

'Hello Hazel, its Jeannie'. I was unsure of what response I would get from the ex-mother-in-law who had always liked me, but who I hadn't seen or spoken to since Anna's ordeal. I prepared myself for a lecture or being ignored through anger. 'Is Mark at yours, please?'

'Hello my duck how are you? I bet you have had a lovely week with your girls together. I know Anna has missed you so much - she always talks about you.' Her tone was kind and sympathetic.

'It's going to be a slow process, but I will get there. Yes, it's been lovely a week thank you. In fact that's why I need to talk to Mark. Is he there yet?'

'He is, my duck I'll get him for you. You take care of yourself and your mum. I hear she has been in hospital. Give her my good wishes and see you soon dear.' Her attitude towards me filled me with humility.

'Hello, Jeannie, everything okay?' The voice of Mark caused the nerves to surface.

'Yes, Mark, it is. That's why I'm ringing: she doesn't want to come home, in fact neither do any of us.' I found it hard to say this to a man that had been so supportive. Quietly, I awaited his reply.

'To be honest, Jeannie I was expecting it. When the phone

rang I knew it was you.' I stayed quiet, holding my breath in anticipation of his reply. 'Well if you can promise me you will never return to Billy, or let him near Anna in the future.'

'I promise that's over. I am going to court to stop him going near Lilly, so there's no chance he will ever get close to Anna.' I waited with baited breath. I could sense him thinking on the other end of the phone. I turned to look at everyone around the dinner table with all eyes pinned on me. Then the words we had longed to hear came.

'I will bring her things down to your mum's in an hour or two, see you then.'

The expression on my face told the awaiting ears what they wanted to hear. Anna jumped up from the table and danced around the room laughing. Lilly, excited by Anna's elation, climbed down from the table and joined in the dancing and mum stood up and hugged me as I replaced the telephone receiver. The kitchen was full of happiness that filled our hearts with joy. Finally my children were with me - something I had yearned for since Anna left four months previously. I felt a very lucky woman. For the next few months Anna, Lilly and I shared mum's double bed: it is a memory all three of us remember to this day. It was then I began to sleep and recover from the damage Billy had done to us.

The following week brought a letter from Mrs Radford requesting me to make an appointment with her secretary with a view to discussing the finalisation of the custody and access hearing in regards to Lilly. The date had been set for the second week in November, just two weeks away.

Sitting in her office, I was shocked to be told I must be open to the fact Billy had rights to access to his daughter, and although she believed every word I said and that Lilly could be in danger, I had no proof and courts work on proof, not on what the warring parents say against each other. As for the ordeal pertaining to Anna, because it wasn't reported to the authorities there was no actual proof of who had beaten her and neither was there any intervention by the police in regard to my treatment by him.

She advised me that, with the courts involved, he would be immediately arrested and imprisoned if he harmed Lilly in any way. I couldn't believe what I was hearing; he was being given a chance to hurt my daughter, just so the court could be sure he was a danger. The threats to her life meant nothing to them, as they thought they were mere idle threats in an argument. I sat amazed and shocked as I listened and she saw the concern in my face.

'Jeannette, if we are ultimately going to protect Lilly we have to show the courts we are not doing this vindictively. I do have a few things up my sleeve, but you have to be seen to be putting Lilly first. I will suggest him seeing her at a contact centre so he is not alone with her and also that he has no contact if he has been drinking. This proviso shows you're willing to bend a little. I am sorry because it's not what you want, but the courts see it as in the best interest of the child. It is very rare a court will revoke all rights of the father.'

I knew she was finding it hard to be the bearer of such news, as she knew how frightened I was of Billy, but that was the point it was me who was afraid of the man. Lilly had to be given the chance to have a relationship with her father. With reluctance, I agreed to follow her advice.

It wasn't a day I relished. I had to go against my better judgement and give in to what the courts decided was in their minds the best thing for my child. I had never broken the law and although I had attended court access hearings over Anna, I knew this was not going to be an easy day. On arriving at the court, Mrs Radford greeted me as I entered the waiting room. I saw Billy at the end of the room sitting alone - as he turned his head, I saw him grinning the way he did when he knew he was in control. She was right: no matter what I said to the magistrates, they allowed his access to Lilly. They did, however, make stipulations that he was not to drink alcohol during or before his access and for the next twelve weeks he was to see Lilly at an access centre in the city every two weeks for three hours, every second Saturday between the hours of 2 and 5 pm. This went some way to ease my worry over her safety. Mrs Radford had done the best she could for the moment and I had two weeks to prepare Lilly for her visit with her father. The first visit fell just before her second birthday. On collecting her, she was excited that she had seen her daddy and the volunteer helpers at the contact centre handed me bags of presents and toys she had been given by Billy and his family. I was genuinely pleased the visit went well for her, but still something deep down inside I couldn't shift the little voice that alerted me to it all being a ploy. Her following visit was more or less the same as it was in Christmas week; even more toys and presents were given to her: she was in her element. I noticed this time her grandmother and aunt were in attendance at the centre. Still, though I made a fuss and was happy for Lilly's delight, I couldn't calm this little voice warning me things were not as they seemed. Although I tried to come to terms with the visitations throughout the three months' contact, this feeling wouldn't subside. Eventually the report on the rapport between Lilly and her father was read out at the follow-up court hearing: they saw no detriment to the access continuing outside of the contact centre. My hands were tied - his ploy had worked. Showing the devoted and loving father had hoodwinked everyone concerned, except for Mrs Radford and myself. A court order was made in the respect of Billy's drinking; he was not to drink before or during visitation or take Lilly onto licensed premises and each access visit was to be at his mother's house. As I walked out of the courtroom, Mrs Radford suggested I keep a close eye on Lilly's behaviour on her return from her father's and if I saw anything out of character, to keep an account of it. She knew I was still worried, but for now her hands were tied.

'Ring me immediately if you're worried about anything at all, no matter how small. He may have fooled the courts, but we know the truth. Try and 'stay strong'. She gave me an empathic smile as she said goodbye and left.

With Anna and Lilly on access visits to their respective fathers every Sunday, life began to settle down. Both girls seemed happy and always looked forward to coming back to me and their mamma's at teatime and over tea we would have a general discussion on their individual days out. It was an ideal time for mum and me to spend time together. We would go to the cinema or out for a meal, recapturing the friendship we had when I was a teenager, before I left home to marry Mark at seventeen. I did all I could to accept the situation and Lilly seemed to be happy with the arrangements - that was 'til a few weeks later. Lilly started to look a little sad when Sundays arrived, which was unusual because she had been enjoying the days with her father. I asked if anything was wrong and she said,

'Not really, mummy.'

'So what is it?' I asked her quietly and calmly, hoping she would open up to me.

'I just want to stay with you, mummy.'

I explained to her how she had to go to see her father and unless he was nasty or hurt her, I couldn't keep her away from him. If I did I would be in trouble. She smiled and said,

'I will go, mummy.'

I was very uneasy all day that Sunday and couldn't wait to fetch her home. I waited as usual at the gate but no-one arrived; after a few minutes I heard her calling me as she came running down the road, followed by Billy. I hugged her and took her bag off her and began the walk to mum's without a word spoken to Billy. I avoided contact with him at all times; he was supposed to see Lilly at his mother's. Trying to not make a big deal of it, I asked if she had been out for a walk or the park.

'No, mummy, I've been at Natalie's playing with her little girls we went to the pub.'

'Natalie? What and daddy?' I questioned her, not making it sound like I was annoyed.

'Yes Natalie is daddy's friend she's got two little girl and a big girl they're my friends. We had pop and daddy and Natalie had big beer.' In her innocence she had just informed me of my worst fear: Billy was drinking around her. I let the subject drop and as we walked through the park she played on the swings until we saw Anna being bought back by Mark. Anna ran to join us, and with a wave of acknowledgement, Mark turned and returned home. We had half an hour playing on the swings and walked across the road to mum's. Tea was on the table waiting for us, so we all had our meal with lots of stories of what the girls had been doing on their day out. Mum's face turned serious as Lilly recounted her day at the pub. As mum looked at me, I nodded - she took on board I didn't want to make a fuss at that particular time. The following morning, I made it the first priority to ring Mrs Radford. After our conversation about the previous day's revelations, she advised me to stop access at once and come in the following Thursday for a full account of Lilly's visit. She also advised me she had written to me in connection to the repossession of 202. I thanked her for her help on both matters and said I would see her on the following Thursday.

Mum, Lilly and I set off for the city and soon arrived at Mrs Radford's office. Sitting in the waiting room, I was convinced this time Billy would lose access rights - after all, he had broken all terms of the court order. In the meeting with her, Mrs Radford agreed I was quite right and wrote down all I could remember of Lilly's conversation with me and my mother. While I was there I asked about changing Lilly's surname. After my divorce to Mark, I had gone back to my maiden name and due to the fact Billy and I had never married, I could legally do this without his permission. She put the wheels in motion and I signed the deed poll papers to legally use my maiden name of Preston for both Lilly and me. Next we discussed what would happen at court for the repossession of 202, which she explained very well and allayed any worries I had. Before leaving, I asked if I had to do anything legally to stop Billy's access.

'No,' she answered. 'He has broken the terms of the court order - let him make the first step to the court to re-instate the visitation rights, then we have got him. Don't worry.'

I thanked her and she escorted me to the waiting room,

'Is this Lilly?' she asked, 'and this is your mother?'

'Yes. Lilly come and say hello to Mrs Radford.'

'Hello, little lady,' she smiled, then turning to mum she said 'hello; very nice to meet you' as she shook mum's hand. We said our goodbyes and said we would inform each other of any further events. We carried on into the city for lunch and had a good day shopping.

Repossession

It was nerve-racking being in the courtroom on this occasion. With mum looking after Lilly, I had made the journey alone, knowing I was probably going to come face-to-face with Billy and I felt very vulnerable. I looked around the courtroom, with its highly polished oak bench for the judge and a witness box just to the side of it. There was a court usher busying himself around, placing paperwork on desks and water bottles and glasses in front of myself and the table opposite and lastly, one on the bench for the judge. Mrs Radford told me she wouldn't be there that day, but one of her associates would introduce themselves. I looked around the room in the hope of seeing this associate, but all I could see were two burly men sitting at the back of the room which unnerved me. The lady in question eventually arrived and made herself known to me.

'Court rise,' cried the usher.

The door at the front of the room opened. I took a gulp of air as I saw the grey-wigged man enter the room, dressed in a bright red robe with a long white collar. He looked over his small rimmed spectacles as he made his way to the large, old-fashioned, throne- like green leather seat before me.

'I only see one young lady before me - has the defendant arrived yet?' The manner of this man made me feel glad I was not on the receiving end of his wrath.

'No, your Worship, I'm afraid he hasn't,' replied the usher.

'Please be seated,' said the judge, as he continued to look in my direction.

Sitting in a court before a wigged judge, I felt a little scared and intimidated.

'Don't be afraid of me, miss, I will not hurt you.' He must have sensed my slight trepidation. Suddenly he took off his wig: 'there,' he said, 'I am only human, just a man.'

When I looked at this small old man, who could have been anyone's grandfather, he looked less intimidating and I instantly began to relax.

'Now then, young lady, why don't you begin to explain what made you leave your property and what is preventing you from returning to have to ask for a court order to be made?'

'I am at my mother's at the moment, but would like to return home someday to get my daughters settled into some sort of normality. I left my home under the threat of extreme violence …' I explained a brief outline of Billy's behaviour towards my children and myself and that I had been warned by the police and my solicitor to remove him through the court, in order to prevent his return and assure our safety.

'I see,' he said, as he peered into the file before him. The courtroom was silent. After a few minutes the judge replaced his wig and looked directly at me, but I wasn't any longer afraid of him.

'Now then Miss, I am making an order for Mr Burnshaw to quit the residence 202. Please give it a week or so in order for it to be served before you attempt to return. Has he molested you since you ceased living there?'

'He hasn't had the chance, sir, but he did come to my parents' and attack my mother with a glass bottle.'

He returned to his paperwork for a few minutes, then raising his head he said,

'I have also made a non-molestation order: this means if he so much as touches you in any way, or looks at you in a threatening manner, he will be thrown into prison. Now you go back to your mother's house and take care and don't hesitate to contact the police if you need to, immediately telling them you have a non-molestation order.' He smiled and made his way back through the door from whence he came. I left the court with renewed confidence.

Unfortunately the court order had to be personally served on Billy and with no-one knowing what he looked like, as there were no photographs of him available, I had no choice but to be part of the serving party. An officer who worked for Mrs Radford, called Elizabeth, contacted me to enable her to locate

Billy. Visiting me at mum's one evening, she convinced me it was the quickest way of finding him, so I agreed to help. The first place in our search was 202.

'Don't be afraid,' she said. 'I will protect you. I may be little but I am trained to protect myself and a client against these kinds of people. If he so much as looks at me funny I can have him locked away.'

It wasn't his looks she should be afraid of, I thought, but decided to trust her anyway.

On arrival at 202, I anxiously walked behind Elizabeth as we crossed the threshold of the little green council gate. This time it closed quietly. Following her down the path, I remembered my escape that September teatime and it made me shudder. Elizabeth asked permission to enter the house. I couldn't speak as my nerves took over. I nodded in approval.

I could smell the stench of stale cigarettes and alcohol as the door opened. It was icy cold inside even though it was now springtime. Instinctively, I went to the meter in the cupboard. Elizabeth saw it was broken. She got out a writing pad and pen and made a note of it.

'All damage has to be noted, so you won't be charged or prosecuted for it.' I didn't make any comment. She looked in the teapot, I thought that strange.

'It's full of mould,' she said, as she asked me to look into it. She made another note. She opened the fridge; it was empty except for a half-full bottle of sickly-smelling, sour milk. I reached down to take it out.

'Don't touch it', she said sharply. 'Don't touch anything, not yet. I'll go check if he is upstairs.'

I was sure he wasn't, knowing if he had heard me downstairs that he would have immediately attempted to cause some problems, especially since the stopping of access to Lilly. I followed behind her, up the familiar stairs to the bedroom. When she asked me to open the cupboard that housed his clothes, I remarked,

'Most of his clothes have gone.' Another note was jotted in her book.

'Right,' she said, 'get some bags. Fill them with everything that remains here of his. I'm not supposed to help, but give me some bags too - let's get rid of him. Do you have a shed?'

'No, but there's an outside toilet,' I answered.

'That will do. Now, quickly don't leave anything of his in this house, absolutely nothing. We don't want to give him any excuse to break in, which he has a right to do if his belongings are in here.'

We worked quickly. I pointed things out, she would bag them. She went into the bathroom and got his toothbrush and shaving equipment. I emptied his cupboards, clothes from the wardrobe and the washing basket, mixing dirty clothes with clean. When I was happy I had everything of his in the bags, we made our way to the kitchen. She dumped her two bags on the floor and sat at the table and took out her notebook to make even more notes. All the time I was worried he would come round the corner and see what we were doing. I felt sick with fear as the house of hell bought back uneasy memories. I wanted to get out of the house, but Elizabeth seemed quite calm.

'Right by law I cannot take his belongings out of the door; that's your job. Can you manage to put everything in the outside loo? Do you have any keys to the door locks?'

'Yes,' I said. 'When I left, I found every one and took them with me - he has been unable to lock me out.'

'Excellent. Now take the bags out there's nothing else is there? Like books, pictures, anything at all? If there is, he can fight in court for access into the property.'

'No, nothing that's everything I'm sure.'

I hurriedly put the bags, his tools, everything he had left, into the outside toilet. There was more than I thought, causing me to struggle as I squeezed it into the small area. Elizabeth appeared by my side and seeing me struggle she kicked the full bin liners into the toilet and pulled the door closed.

'I didn't do that,' she said with a smile on her face.

We returned to the kitchen, where I asked what she had been writing.

'When we entered, you said immediately that it looked like he had left anyway, so I checked various things like the fridge, cupboards and the teapot is always a dead giveaway that no-one is living here. I also made notes of the damaged electricity meter so you won't be held responsible. Here's my reference number; quote it when you ring the Electricity Board and they will fix it free of charge. Now then, where is he likely to be?'

'The pub,' I instantly replied, shrugging my shoulders, 'but I don't know which one.'

'Come on then, Jeannie, a pub crawl it is.' Her attitude was cheerful but serious.

We left the house and I locked it up, locking him out forever. We made our way over to the club he frequented, but unfortunately he wasn't there. Everyone there was happy to see me, but puzzled why I was asking for Billy. The manager said he hadn't been in for a few days. I asked if he came in during the next few days would he give him a message.

'Happily my dear.' His tone was full of intrigue.

With everyone listening and curious as to why I was searching for Billy, I decided to turn and face the room full of people who knew I had escaped him and who all knew how he had treated me. My lips were quivering as I nervously stated,

'Anyone who sees Billy, would you please tell him his belongings are in the outside toilet? If he hasn't collected them by Tuesday next week, they will be put out for the dustbin men.'

The room roared as there were cheers and shouts of 'well done' followed by whistles and applause. Tears appeared in my eyes their support was invaluable because it gave me confidence to find him and finish the job. We travelled around the pubs in the area. It was a Monday night so they weren't very busy, which made looking for him easier. We parked in the car park at the rear of a popular haunt of his. Elizabeth suggested,

'We will go in the front door and walk straight through to the back entrance. I will be right behind you. If you see him, make a mental note of where he is, and who he is with so I get the right man: don't speak to anyone.'

I followed her instructions. I got a burning of nerves in my stomach making me aware this time I would find him: instinct told me to be careful (a feeling that would warn me of his presence for years to come). I knew the layout of this pub very well, as it was a place I frequented in my teenage years. I walked along the bar which was positioned in the centre of the room. I slowly concentrated on a group sitting down at the tables to the right at the end of the bar. Sure enough there he was, sitting with a crowd of people with a girl next to him. I took notice of what she was wearing: I knew her personally and recognised this was the Natalie that Lilly had been referring to. My heart was racing; my legs felt like jelly and my mouth dried with nerves the instant I saw his face. He saw me walking towards him and looked at me in shock, which quickly turned to anger as I continued past him followed by Elizabeth, making my way through to the back door and out into the car park. Elizabeth recognised my demeanour had changed so she closely stuck by me until we reached her car. She opened the passenger door as quick as she could and I climbed inside. Getting into the driver's seat she said,

'Try to calm down - I won't let him near you. These bullies rarely attack a stranger. Take a few minutes to catch your breath then tell me which one he is.'

I gave her his description and his position, although she had gathered by my reaction his whereabouts. I explained what the girl next to him was wearing and told her that her name was Natalie. She took the papers to be served out of her bag, holding them tightly in her hand. She got out of her car saying,

'Stay there, don't get out or open the door to anyone. I won't be long.'

She locked the car behind her, leaving me rigid in my seat wondering what would happen next. I saw her go round to the front of the pub to retrace our steps. Within minutes she was out of the back door and coming towards me. She looked very calm she even had a smile on her face. I looked past her expecting Billy to be following behind her; she opened the door and sat down.

'I love the expression they give me when I serve them. I told him he has until Monday to collect his belongings, so keep out of the way. Give it a couple of weeks before you move back in. Just because you have a non-molestation order, it doesn't mean you're safe they are easily ignored.'

How right she was.

The second week in January, I felt ready to move to 202 with the attitude 'a New Year, yet another new start'. Mum had come to terms with dad leaving and although it was hard for her she began to make a life of her own. We discussed my decision and although I was returning home, I would come to mum's regularly to make sure she was coping alone. In the week leading up to our moving-in date I visited the house alone to make the fire, to air the damp that had taken over through being unlived in for a year. I needed a few days to clean the place and get rid of any broken doors etc. trying to eradicate the bad memories, especially for Anna. I informed the police officer in charge of my case of my plans and he said he would meet me there with some information and advice on security and the legalities concerning the court order. After an initial chat, he spent time checking windows and doors. He informed me of what they could do to help keep me safe and of the fact I would be on an immediate response list, meaning if I rang 999 they would come to my aid immediately. After he had left, I locked myself in (something I did for over a year). It was a strange feeling being in 202 alone. My mind relived some of the abuse inflicted on me, in my mind's eye I could see the awful attacks I'd endured as I wandered around room to room. There wasn't one door without punch holes or that wasn't hanging off its hinges where I had held on for dear life to stop him dragging me around the house. The bathroom door was completely off and split. I made the decision to come up for a few days without the girls and redecorate the rooms and get the council to rehang new doors. Our moving-in day arrived and it was with mixed feelings I left mum. I knew she would be alone now for the first time in her life, but I had to make steps to recover my independence and to bring up my girls. The girls were excited about going home, although both Anna and I found it daunting. The redecoration didn't alter the fact that I had almost died in that house on more than one occasion. I had moved Anna into my old bedroom after painting the walls in a pretty pink colour and added another bed for Lilly. I put the double bed in the small room, after painting the walls in warm lilac tones. The downstairs had been scrubbed clean and I had ripped off the devil-red painted wallpaper and chosen a bright white paint and a contrasting flowered paper to replace the red.

The kitchen was a now a welcoming pastel yellow. The house was warm with a glowing fire and the heating warming through the upstairs. The council had happily replaced the damaged doors after I told them of the court order and violence, so all in all on the surface it looked a bright and cheerful home. The girls were happy to be sharing a room together and happily played in there for hours. I finally felt my life was heading in the right direction and I was determined no man would ever hurt me or my children again. My dreams of peace were short-lived. I returned to mum's the following weekend in order to feel safe and so we could be company for each other. The thought of Billy knowing I had returned home scared me, and I feared after his Friday drinking session he would be brave enough to arrive at my door. My instincts were right.

'Billy's at your door yelling and banging; he thinks you're home,' said my neighbour who telephoned me and had been given mum's number in case of emergency.

Thanking her, I immediately rang the police. Our officer was unfortunately on leave, but the computer showed the fact I was on instant response. After making sure I was safe, they dispatched a car to remove him from my property. I was later to find out the court order that had been made wasn't worth the paper it was written on, as it hadn't got a 'power of arrest' attached so in essence I wasn't safe from him at all. For the next two years I lived constantly at mums at the weekends for safety due to his continual harassment, intimidation and threatening behaviour towards me and no-one could do a thing about it.

Cause for Concern

Soon I received a letter from Billy's solicitor who had put me in court for breaking the order of access. Confident, I attended, thinking that because he had broken the order due to drinking and taking her away from his mother's onto licensed premises, his access would be revoked. I was astounded when once again he was given access, albeit back at the access centre. His grin at getting away with disobeying the court order was instant, he thought he could flout the law and get away with it. And he seemed to be right. His usual doting father routine at the access centre again won him out-of-supervision access. It was around a few months into access when Lilly seemed a little subdued on the Sunday morning of her visit to Billy's mam's. Asking her if she wanted to go that day, she unconvincingly replied 'yes', but her whole demeanour was slow and disheartened. I worried for her all the time she was away. The court had made it a proviso he fetch and return Lilly; even though I insisted I had a non-molestation order, I was ignored. I seemed to be getting nowhere with trying to protect my child. This particular day I sat Lilly down on her return from Billy's and asked her directly if her daddy was kind to her.

'Not always, mummy, only when grandma was there.' Her subdued manner worried me so I asked:

'When he upsets you, Lilly, what does he do?' I tried to speak casually to her and draw any information from her.

'He shouts at me all the time.' She looked to the floor. I lifted her face with my hand under her chin - she flinched. I had to be careful not to put thoughts or words in her mind.

'Why? Are you naughty when your grandma's not there?'

'No, mummy, I'm good all the time but he shouts at me anyway. He makes me wear jeans that he bought me and I say I don't want to I want to wear my pretty dress that I go in but he shouts, so I have to wear them.' At this point she started to cry. I held her as she cried and gently said,

'Maybe he just wants you to wear what he bought you. It's only for an hour or so and anyway it will keep your dress nice when you're playing.' She didn't say anything more and as Anna had returned from her dad's, her pleasure of seeing her sister took away her sadness. I realised his bullying behaviour was continuing, albeit only slightly. I knew I had to keep an eye on her. On Christmas Eve I went out with my family - mum, my brothers, their wives and children for a drink. On returning home in a taxi, I noticed the handle of my front door was broken in half. Letting myself in, I asked the girls to wait by the door in case anyone was in the house. Mum had given me an ageing Boxer bitch for protection - I noticed she had gone absolutely crazy scratching at the front door. The neighbour shouted over to me and informed me Billy had just left and had been banging and kicking at the door and shouting obscenities through the letter box, even though my dog was going crazy – it didn't deter him. They had rung the police but as yet they hadn't been. Immediately I rang the police and they said, because I hadn't rung, they hadn't put it down as an emergency but that someone would be down immediately. On their arrival I had packed a bag, put the dog on the lead and was waiting. I insisted they take me to my mother's for safety, which they did. They told me to return to court for an order with attachment for 'power of arrest'. I shrugged my shoulders and said,

'What's the point, the courts don't listen.'

The following Monday I rang Mrs Radford to say I was getting fed up with all his harassment and threats. She immediately told me to stop access, which I happily agreed to do and made another appointment with her to update what had been happening. Lilly was now a little over three years old, and although Billy had access to his little girl, I continued to suffer his bullying for another eighteen months - which consisted of intimidation and vicious threats to my life if I interfered with the visitation rights the court had given him. Once again, I anxiously waited to be summoned back to court.

As expected, four months later, I received a letter from the court. Only this time it was a summons for incarceration with a threat of arrest if I didn't appear. I felt sick. I couldn't believe it: I was a law-abiding citizen trying to protect myself and my girls from all the threats and harassment of this man and I was the one facing prison after everything he had done and continued to do to me and my children. Scared of my fate, I appeared in court. Again Mrs Radford read out the catalogue of intimidation and behaviour, explaining he was the first one to break the court order being told not to drink or take Lilly onto licensed premises. She expressed our concerns about the subdued character Lilly was showing before and after her visits, but still the courts ignored her. They seemed intent on believing the man sitting in the courtroom sneering, with his glaring eyes fixed on mine. Billy was in his element seeing me scared of a prison sentence. I was released with a warning that if I was brought before them again in respect of refusing access to Mr Burnshaw, I would be looking at a custodial sentence. The court ignored the fact Mrs Radford told them I had acted on her instructions. They didn't seem to care. I looked at Billy in dismay; he was laughing for all to see.

"What can I say, Jeannette? I can't believe their thinking - something's definitely not right.' Her concern for my freedom and Lilly's safety was growing. They had, however, asked the court welfare officer to make a report, which meant I would have a chance to tell her my concerns, and then a visit to Billy would be made. I was to wait for the report to be made and then I would be informed of the new arrangements for access. I shook my head in disbelief as I said goodbye to my solicitor and left the building more and more disgusted in the courts and the law.

Mrs Statham was an older lady around 60 years old. Her hair looked like it was regularly set at the hairdresser's and she wore a pale green skirt suit with a darker green blouse underneath, with gold necklaces adorning her attire. Very quietly spoken, she introduced herself as the court welfare officer and believed I was expecting her. She mentioned she had already visited Billy, which informed me I had a hard job on my hands though I soon realised she wasn't there to talk to me: even though she had talked to Billy, her job was to see what Lilly wanted to do. She asked if I would leave the premises so Lilly would feel free to say anything without intimidation and assured me of her safety. I reluctantly agreed and left, going to mum's for twenty minutes. On my return Lilly seemed happy and played with her toys as the officer was writing notes while waiting for me to return. She thanked me for my co-operation and left. Giving Lilly a hug, I joined in her play while mum made a cup of tea.

'What did the lady say Lilly, can you tell me?'

'I have to go and see daddy'. Her attitude was matter of fact.

'Why?' I quizzed her, being a little shocked at her turnaround of attitude.

'Because he's crying,' she said, 'because I don't want to see him.'

Shocked I asked:

'Is that what the nice lady told you?'

'Yes.' She didn't seem thrilled at the idea of going to see Billy and carried on playing.

'That's emotional blackmail,' mum commented on her return from the kitchen.

I agreed. I was furious. I immediately rang Mrs Radford to voice my disgust at the officer's behaviour.

'I have made a note of that, but I must advise you they will probably reinstate his access you must take her if they do. Don't worry; we will work on it after we see her report. I will contact you.'

A few days later, as expected, I was ordered to reinstate Billy's access rights. I explained to Lilly that because she told the lady she wanted to see her daddy, she must now go to see him, but if at any time he frightened or hurt her she was immediately to tell me so I could have a word and make life happier for her. I didn't want her thinking she had to put up with his bullying because he might cry. She was almost four years old now and understood a little more of how she was feeling. For the first few weeks Billy would turn up at the door, knock and then be around halfway up the road before Lilly was out of the gate. It hurt me to see her running after him; I felt she was so unloved by him. Until I had solid evidence, my hands were tied until he damaged her. The court would not listen to either Mrs Radford or me; even the police were at their wits' end with him. What happened next caused the police to try to get him locked away to give me some peace from the on-going intimidation that was starting to drive me into a state of depression.

I heard the girls one morning coming up the stairs arguing who was going to give me a parcel which had been delivered by the postman. Bursting through my bedroom door, both in a state of excitement, Anna asked,

'What have you ordered, mummy?'

'Nothing,' I replied. 'Stop fighting you two, give it here,' I ordered, still dazed by being woken by such a commotion.

'It's got pretty tape on it, mummy,' Lilly remarked. 'What is it?'

'If you give me chance, I will open it and tell you,' I said, taking the parcel out of Anna's hands.

The girls climbed onto the bed, anticipating the surprise wrapped in brown paper and pretty green and yellow tape. My instinct told me to be careful - a sick feeling came over me and l knew something wasn't right. I started to open the package carefully. I sensed something horrific inside the attractive wrapping. I ordered the girls out of the room immediately; slamming the door behind them and leaving them disappointed at not being there at the opening. I could hear them blaming each other in deciding whose fault it was they had been sent out of the room. I prepared myself for the unpleasantness awaiting me as I began to face the contents. A typed note lying between the fold of brown paper said,

'An eye for an eye,' my suspicions were founded as I stared at the package, plucking up enough courage to continue. Holding in a deep breath, I uncovered the goriest thing I had ever seen.

'Yes Billy,' I thought, 'and a tooth for a tooth.'

A pig's eyeball sat staring back at me with all connecting blood vessels and muscles. I re-wrapped it along with the note, trying not to vomit. Once dressed and having had a strong, hot cup of tea I told the girls to get ready we had to go out. They quickly did as asked and we went up to the police station, taking the package with us. As usual in my time of need, the police station was closed but the citizen's advice centre on the opposite side of the road was open. I left the girls in the waiting room, with orders to be good while I went in to see an advisor. Feeling anger, disgust and sickened, I opened the package; showing her first the note. She braced herself for what was about to be revealed, the eyeball. It was at that point I broke down crying this felt like the last straw. I couldn't cope anymore. Billy's intimidation was getting out of hand. The advisor went to make me a cup of tea, giving me time to compose my demeanour. On her return she mentioned,

'Your daughters are sitting happily looking at magazines they are okay. Sit there a few minutes and drink your tea because you must be in shock. I will ring the police.'

'I went there first - there is no-one there,' I said through the tears.

'There will be; they just haven't opened the door yet,' she replied.

I heard her telling an officer about what she had seen - then she said,

'Give her five minutes as you can imagine she's in a bit of a state. Thank you, goodbye.'

When my composure returned, I left the office to go over the road where our officer was waiting for me. He had heard the complaint over the phone and recognised my name, so he took over the interview. There was more strong tea waiting for me as he asked me to tell him what had happened, which I did.

'Any other enemies?' He asked, 'other than Billy?'

'Not that I know of,' I felt very dejected and frightened by the fact someone went to these lengths to threaten me.

We went through the people I knew who would be capable of getting hold of a pig's eye. Two of Billy's brothers were slaughter-men - but then - my own brother was a manager at three around the area. They intended visiting the brothers, including my own, and they were to be finger-printed to see if they matched the one on the package. Though the police seriously believed it was sent by Billy - their ploy was for the time being to ignore Billy's involvement. They believed that, as word went around his family, he wouldn't be able to resist walking into the police station demanding his prints be taken. They were right. Within a few days Billy rushed to the police station, demanding they interview him and take his prints. They refused. Billy had been drinking - he was belligerent which led him to being cautioned in an attempt to calm him down. He didn't - so he was immediately arrested. The police were then able to bail him on condition he stayed away from me and my address, which bought me a little peace to get over the shock. Contacting Mrs Radford I explained what had happened and she immediately prepared papers for the court in respect of threatening behaviour and intimidation – hoping this would help in our custody case proving harassment. On this occasion my brother Dean, concerned for my safety, drove me to a local court where the case was to be heard. While Dean parked the car I made my way into the reception where I was greeted by Mrs Radford's associate, who had accompanied me on the case to repossess 202. I was directed to the courtroom. I noticed two burly men sitting at the rear of the courtroom. I realised every time I had attended a court hearing these same two men were in attendance. I asked my solicitor who they were.

'They are your bodyguards. They will protect you at every court appearance.' I realised at that point my fears were believed. It was at that point I realised how seriously Mrs Radford took my word and was doing all she could to protect me from any attacks from Billy.

Suddenly a wigged barrister walked into the courtroom and sat in the chair in the front of me. Turning around - he introduced himself. This time a serious assault with evidence; a pig's eyeball sent through the Queen's Royal Mail. I had a barrister who was intent on prosecuting Billy. By the time the judge had taken his seat, Billy hadn't yet made his appearance. The doors opened and in walked my brother. The judge assumed it was Billy and sternly began to question him to his name. I spoke up and told the judge it was my brother - who was there to support me. The judge duly apologised to Dean and turned to Billy's solicitor asking him why he was being made to wait. Then the courtroom doors were flung open - causing everyone to turn around. There stood Billy.

'Are you William Burnshaw?' The voice of the judge was sharp and powerful.

Billy didn't look so self-assured anymore, nor did he look the big menacing bully. He was lost for words as he stood meekly before the judge. It was then I saw a weak pathetic man who this time wasn't going to laugh me out of court.

'Think yourself lucky you are not heading straight for the cells. Now sit down.' The judge exercised his authority loudly and clearly.

Billy, quiet and embarrassed, took a seat at the side of his solicitor. Though there was no actual proof that Billy had sent the pig's eye, my solicitor took it on herself to send documents of the trauma I had suffered at his hands - to the court via the barrister. Billy's disobedience of the non-molestation court order and the continuous harassment he had caused me was clearly made known to the judge. After a few questions and the continuous denial of the pig incident, Billy sounded flustered and unsure of his freedom - after arriving late. The judge turned to me and asked,

'Does this person still cause you to be afraid by his behaviour towards you?'

'Yes, Your Worship, I'm terrified of him,' I admitted.

Mr Burnshaw, stand up,' he ordered. 'I will warn you now - whether you sent this diabolical thing to this young lady or not; if you are brought before me or any other judge in connection of violence, harassment or intimidation to this lady - believe me - you will go immediately to the cells for a very long time. Do you understand?'

Billy foundered as he replied 'Yes – sir.'

'I do not tolerate such behaviour. Case dismissed.'

Everyone in the courtroom stood as the judge retired to his chambers. Billy immediately left the courtroom, his face pale and stunned. I sat for a while - on the instructions of the barrister, to enable Billy to leave the building. Dean joined me and listened as I was warned to be very careful when leaving the building. Dean was advised to fetch the car up to the doors of the building. Once he had arrived, the bodyguards would escort me to his waiting car. Dean left me in their safe hands - realising now - the serious danger I had been in over the last three years.

'Mrs Radford will be in touch as soon as I have informed her of the outcome - until then - stay safe,' explained the barrister.

I thanked my stand-in solicitor and the barrister as I made my way towards the burly bodyguards waiting for me and keeping an eye out for Billy's return - by the entrance door. Dean pulled up and I was duly escorted to the car - I thanked security.

'He's just gone in the pub next to the car park, Jeannie, so be careful tonight. 'Dean's concerns were obvious, after witnessing the judge's threat of prison for Billy.

'I'm stopping with mum tonight - the girls are with her now.' Dean nodded in approval and relief.

The following Sunday Lilly was crying and begged me not to send her to Billy's. When I asked her why she didn't want to go, she said,

'He hurts me mummy, and grandad does. Then daddy laughs at me when I cry.' She threw her arms around my waist as she sobbed and begged me once more. A lump appeared in my throat; the thought of her being bullied and hurt cut me to the quick.

'How long as daddy been hurting you?'

'For age's mummy - he pulls the hairs on my legs because they're hairy and it hurts and when I cry he shouts at me. Then grandad laughs and he does it too. They scare me, mummy, please, please don't make me go.' She became distraught. I comforted her promising she didn't have to go but she had to be telling me the truth.

'I am, mummy I promise. I never want to go again.' Her sobbing continued. I sat her on my knee and comforted her until she calmed down and was a little more audible.

'Lilly, has daddy ever hit you?' She was quiet for a few minutes then murmured,

'He only smacks me - when I'm naughty.'

'What do you do to be naughty?' I was being careful not to put suggestions in her mind.

'I don't eat my dinner at grandma's house because I'm not hungry.'

'Why don't you eat your dinner, sweetheart, don't you like it?'

'It's not that. I have dinner with Natalie because daddy's at the pub. Natalie takes me to grandma's house and I have to eat another one or he smacks me.'

'Why didn't you tell me this before, Lilly?'

'I was frightened.'

'Frightened? What - of me?'

'No, mummy, daddy said if I cried and told you, then you will have to go to prison and then I have to live with him, don't go to prison, mummy. I hate him - he scares me. I don't want to go to him. Please.'

Her outburst was very alarming and upsetting. I wondered how long she had felt like this. I remembered her being subdued at times, but until she told me I couldn't do anything about it. I stroked her hair and looked at the clock, it was almost 10.30 am. I knew either he or Natalie would soon be on their way. I took control and fired up for a battle.

'Go to your room, Lilly. You're not in any trouble, but daddy will be here soon - stay in your room 'til I fetch you.' Her skinny little legs scurried as fast as they could carry her up the stairs as I waited on tenterhooks. Sitting on the bottom step of the stairs facing the glass panel of the door I waited for the knock. Within minutes Billy's thump rattled the wooden frame. Full of foreboding, I slightly opened the door to see Billy standing at the gate - looking for his daughter.

'She's not coming,' I calmly told him 'and she won't be coming anymore.'

He glared at me, his top lip curled under, showing his top set of tobacco stained teeth. He chillingly laughed,

'See you in court.'

Let Battle Commence

The following Sunday arrived and the telephone rang about 10am.

'Hi, Jeannie, it's Natalie. I was just checking to see if Lilly was coming today?'

'No, Natalie, she won't be coming again - hasn't Billy told you?'

'No, he's still in bed. He never tells me anything except he didn't think she was coming, so I thought I'd ask you.'

'To be honest, Natalie, she says she doesn't want to come any more - she gets upset because he shouts at her for not eating her dinner at his mam's.'

'I keep telling him she can't go all day without her dinner while he's in the pub, so I feed her here with my kids, then he expects her to eat another one; he should take her at dinnertime if he wants her to eat there.'

'So he's still in bed, then.' I found myself starting to interrogate her. I needed all the information I could possibly get. 'Was it a heavy drinking session last night then?' Trying to keep a friendly demeanour as I politely questioned her. I needed details; I knew I had a fight on my hands and the need to beat this man was imperative.

'It was, as usual, and I took the brunt of it because Lilly wasn't coming today.'

'I'm sorry, Natalie, but I have to protect her.'

'Of course you do - we both know what he's like.'

'Is she normally with you on a Sunday then?'

'Yeah 'til he comes home from pub about 3pm then he sleeps it off and he takes Lilly with him to his mam's for dinner.'

'Doesn't he ever take her with him to the club?'

'Sometimes, but you know him always penniless, so she stays with me. My kids love her being here – they all play together nice.'

I was pleased she was with other children, but the information she gave me was invaluable. She seemed happy to have someone to talk to and easily offered up the information.

'Right, I'd better go; he will be up soon, the pub will be open. Thanks for the chat.'

Oh, thank you, I thought. We said our goodbyes and I picked up a pen and paper and wrote down everything she had said. This time he had broken three of the conditions: he was to see her at his mam's house and he wasn't allowed to drink alcohol during access hours - or take her onto licensed premises. I had begun my own investigation and after seeing him belittled by the judge over the pig's eye - I realised he was not that big. This new-found confidence was to help over the next few months - I knew I had to 'stay strong'.

I waited for the court date to arrive - this time I was sure I had enough for the magistrates to take notice of my concerns. The court letter arrived - I was shocked to see it was another committal hearing to incarcerate me for disobeying the court order for Billy's access. This infuriated me; I had actually expected an access hearing requested by Mrs Radford. Billy had disobeyed the court orders from the beginning, but never got as much as a slap on the wrists. I began to feel like the world was against me and after all he had put me and the girls through, he was still in control and the courts were helping him to ruin our lives. I remembered the last committal hearing and had been warned I would be going to prison if I disobeyed again for whatever reason. My confidence took a blow - I was sure I would be going to prison. This time - I was flatly going to refuse him access - whatever the outcome. I asked mum if she would be alright to watch Lilly for me for a couple of hours - I had something I must do and needed to be alone to concentrate.

'Of course I can, but where are you going?'

'I'm off up to the library.'

Lilly wasn't quite in school yet, though she attended playschool a few mornings a week. I had informed them of the problems with her father and that under no circumstances should they allow him near her. It would only be a few more weeks until Lilly, at four-and-a-half years old, would be in school full-time. I desperately wanted everything sorted out before her schooling began. Walking into the library - I immediately went upstairs to find reference books about family law. I sat at a desk and took out a pen and paper out of my bag. I didn't know where to start, but intended spending as much time as it took to learn the law on Custody and Access to a Minor. First, I began to read about cases where children had gone to the respective parent and abuse of that child had continued until death, resulting in imprisonment for the abuser. This didn't help except to make me more determined to win my daughter away from Billy once and for all. I spent the hours reading, finding out my rights as the custodial parent. Then I read up on Billy's rights. To my amazement, I read that because Billy and I were not married, the only rights he had was what I - or the court - would give him. I made a note of that. Also, I read that a violent and abusive parent would, in most cases, lose the right of access - only in exceptional circumstances would they be given access and only under supervision. I knew the court had a process to follow, but how on earth could the magistrates on the basis of two hours every other week of supervised access; judge him not to be of danger to anyone? Of course he would be on his best behaviour. I continued to make notes. I felt empowered to be reading about a subject the courts thought they had all the answers to. Mistakes had been made, resulting in harm and fatalities. I was not only taking on Billy; now I was fighting the law.

While I was at the library, my sister-in-law Ellen came to visit my mother. They had obviously been chatting about the situation between Billy and me - in my absence. I joined in the conversation on arrival at mums - explaining all I had learnt.

The day for the committal hearing arrived. I knew this time I was probably going to be put in prison. The magistrates don't look lightly on people who ignore them. Unless you are Billy - it seemed. I had to decide what was to happen with Lilly if I was to be imprisoned. Arrangements had to be made to keep her safe and out of Billy's reach. It was a hard decision to make, but I knew I had to end this cycle of abuse and torment we had found ourselves in. I contacted someone who Billy didn't know and who I trusted impeccably. They weren't local - but Lilly loved them very much and after their offer to help - I decided to ask them to take care of her - if the worst happened. Lilly was to join them until I was released or other arrangements could be made. I knew it wouldn't be long before my mum and Mrs Radford had worked to release me, but I wasn't going to prison for Lilly to be taken into the custody of Billy. Arrangements were sorted and Lilly was told she might have to go on holiday soon without me - until I came for her; she understood what I meant. Next, I prepared to face the courts.

The court building looked very daunting to me today. I was accompanied by mum and a friend who drove us there. I hesitated before I walked in the doors; I felt my spirit ebbing away after all the browbeating of magistrates and court welfare officers. I knew Mrs Statham's report would have been read by the court and Billy would be in his element at the thought I would be out of the way - for his possession of Lilly. I took in a deep breath and I forced my jellied legs through the shiny glass door. I searched unconsciously for Mrs Radford, but my eyes could not find her - my heart began to sink. Though I tried to keep an outwardly tough demeanour - I struggled to follow my companions to a seat in the waiting area.

'Ms Preston.' The voice of the quietly spoken Mrs Statham addressed me. 'Would you like to come into the interview room and have a private chat with Mr Burnshaw about how to come to some arrangement over Lilly?'

For a second I couldn't believe what she was saying - but for some unknown reason I turned to her - looked down the room and saw Billy's condescending face and without thinking I replied,

'Yes.'

She signalled Billy to enter the interview room. As I walked in its direction I saw the two bodyguards' dumbstruck expressions. I didn't look back to see mum's reaction, though I knew inside she would be worried. Every other time I had been asked into a private interview with Billy I had refused due to my fear of him - but this time I felt different. I let Billy enter the room first.

It was a tiny square room with three chairs facing each other. Billy stood tall and intimidating with his slimy grin showing his top teeth. I faced him - eye to eye. I didn't flinch. Mrs Statham instantly regretted her clever idea.

'Now then,' she said, 'who would like to begin?' Her voice drifted into oblivion as she tried to convince us it was in Lilly's best interest to talk.

'You're going down - you stupid bitch.' He kicked the chair in front of him as he ended his threat.

I didn't remove my eyes from his, but in my peripheral vision I saw the expression of the small, fragile, court welfare officer's face. For the first time she had seen the real Billy - his intimidating nasty attitude. I stood firm as I replied,

'You don't scare me anymore, Billy - bring it on.'

Mrs Statham stood in total shock, realising that Billy wasn't the nice, charming man he had led her to believe. It was too late: her report had been accepted and read by the magistrates. She asked us to leave the room as she grew panicky as she sensed the hatred between us. For a few minutes we stood locked into a stare. I was determined he wasn't going to win this, not this time. She opened the door, instantly, shot one of the bodyguards and stood between Billy and me. I walked out of the room. I scanned the waiting room for Mrs Radford. I saw the relief on everyone's face as I walked towards mum - unharmed. I had to 'stay strong' and take the fight within me into the courtroom. My solicitor, who had heard I was in the interview room, rushed over to me.

'I'm sorry,' she said, 'they have revoked your legal aid as it's your second committal hearing. I'm not allowed in court.' I felt my heart sinking and for a split second I felt defeated. She continued, 'I will ask permission of the magistrates to speak on your behalf. How did it go in there?'

Finding some strength from deep within, I replied,

'I'm going to beat him, one way or another.'

As I entered the court I was immediately taken to the dock - I felt like a criminal. It was then the reality of the situation hit me. There was no seat to sit on and no Bible to on which to swear an oath. I began to feel like the criminal the system was turning me in to. No-one else but Billy, his solicitor, Mrs Statham and I were allowed in the courtroom. Mrs Radford walked beside me.

The magistrates were already seated at the bench and I felt all eyes were on me. I looked at them and nervously smiled as they asked my name. Mrs Radford then spoke.

'Your Honours, I ask permission to address you.'

'Mrs Radford,' the head magistrate answered, 'we were led to believe there would be no representation for this lady due to the nature of the hearing being a committal hearing.'

'Yes, that's right, your honour,' she replied. 'This is no ordinary case of disobedience or ignoring the court order. I feel she needs someone to speak on her behalf and I am willing to represent her off the record and free of charge, if your Honours would give me your permission.'

The three magistrates conferred between themselves as I nervously awaited the outcome. They looked at me and then they granted Mrs Radford's wishes.

She began by explaining why this case was not a simple case of me disrespecting the courts and that I had a genuine fear for my daughter's safety, in fact for both my daughters. She told them she was speaking on my behalf free of charge - because she felt there was a great injustice happening to my family. She asked them to give me a chance to tell them why I felt the way I did. She said she totally believed in the fact I was acting in the best interest of my children and that my daughter was, at the last meeting with Mrs Statham, emotionally blackmailed into believing her father was crying because I wouldn't let her go to visit him - otherwise Lilly may have given reasons for not wanting to go to see Mr Burnshaw.

The magistrates looked at me and then at Billy. They saw he was grinning. He sat slouched in his seat, showing no regard for where he was or why we were there. I knew his whole aim was to get me out of the way, so Lilly could be his. But his main aim was to have me put in prison - to enable him to regain control of my life. During my questioning, I could sense Billy's eyes boring into me in an attempt of intimidation. He was hoping I would be too scared to cross him. I watched as Mrs Radford took a seat at the side of Billy's solicitor. Though afraid, I knew I had to be strong and fight for my child. I turned to the bench and took a deep breath as their questioning commenced.

'Could you tell us in your own words why you feel Lilly is in danger from her father?' said the lady magistrate in the middle of the three on the bench.

'We, my children and I, were put through a life of violence and abuse at his hands for more than two years. Since we escaped in September '85 he has continually harassed me; this involved breaking a 100-yard non-molestation order. He continued to come to my home after he had been drinking and tried to break into my house. One Christmas Eve, he actually snapped the metal door handle in an attempt to get to me.'

'So you have been apart over three years now?'

'Yes sir,' I replied to the male sitting on the right of the lady questioning me.

'Since the separation I have taken Lilly on numerous occasions to see him. Thinking he would be sober as the initial court order told him not to drink alcohol or go on to licensed premises while he had her. He always ignored that order. Lilly has come home on various occasions telling me he frightens her. I know how nasty and violent he becomes when he drinks, hence the court order, which he totally disregards.'

'Has Lilly ever come home harmed in any way?' Asked the lady magistrate, with the look of authority her position exuded.

'She has returned in tears on many occasions, relieved to be home. I asked her what was wrong and she said her grandad keeps pulling the hairs on her legs and makes fun of her because her little legs are hairy.'

'But no physical harm?'

'I think hurting a child in any way is physical harm - after all, she has seen and received violence from him in the past.' I knew they were not hearing what I was saying.

I looked across at Mrs Radford, who could not intervene at that point. I glanced over at Billy. His smirk was saying everything; he nodded as if to repeat his earlier words, 'You're going down'.

I continued.

'Why am I in the dock to be committed to prison, when all I am trying to do is protect my daughter? He beat my eldest daughter so badly she was black and blue and had to go to live at her father's for her safety. He can't stay away from alcohol; he breaks the court order continually.' I was trying not to get angry because I didn't want to look like a vindictive ex, then from nowhere I warned, 'put me in prison, but I will tell you now, you won't find Lilly. I would rather stay in prison for the rest of my life than let that monster continue frightening and abusing that little girl. You don't know him.'

I shut up and refused to continue.

Mrs Radford stood up.

'Your Honours. I have worked with this young lady for the last three years. I have found her honest and accommodating in every way to enable access to Mr Burnshaw even though she was terrified, and all because she has been made to do so by the courts. Mr Burnshaw has ignored the courts more than she as and yet she - a mother who is trying to protect her children - one of which was seriously beaten but has since been returned to her by the child's father on condition she has no further contact to Mr Burnshaw, is being threatened with a custodial sentence. This does not show a woman of scorn and vindictiveness, but a caring, frightened mother.'

Mrs Radford sat down.

I looked at the magistrates who could wreck our lives even further. I admit I was afraid for my and my girl's future. I turned away from the gaze of the magistrates. I looked at Billy. He was actually laughing. I shook my head in bewilderment at his contempt.

I heard one of the magistrates say to the others,

'We do have the report from the welfare officer.'

'May I speak?' I asked.

'Of course,' replied the lady magistrate who had kept quiet through the hearing.

'When Mrs Statham came to visit, she insisted I left the home, which I regret doing. She emotionally blackmailed Lilly into saying she wanted to see her daddy by saying - and I quote "your daddy is crying because you won't go to see him". What a thing to say to a child: she is bound to feel bad and go, even if she is scared of him. The child is four years' old.'

I saw their faces change and underneath their spectacles they glanced in the direction of Mrs Statham - who sat with her head bowed. With a more serious demeanour, I watched as they conferred for a few minutes. I was praying silently inside that someone would believe me. After a few minutes the gentleman spoke, his expression mellowing a little.

'You're serious about going to prison rather than Mr Burnshaw seeing his daughter - aren't you?'

'Yes.' My reply was short but firm.

They again conferred. I looked across to my solicitor and she nodded confidently. I saw Billy out the corner of my eye: his face had turned to anger, gone was his inane grin. I returned to look at the bench as the gentleman prepared to speak to me.

'We believe, you seriously think your daughter is in danger from this man. But without any evidence of his violence or disregard of his court orders, our hands are tied.'

Again the man turned to his associates, whispering so no-one could overhear. The silence in the court was almost deafening. I stood feeling like a criminal in the dock. All three magistrates faced me - their eyes seem to pierce my soul.

'If we gave you a day in court, where you will have the whole day to state your case, would that be amenable to you?' said the man who had seemed to have taken the main control of my questioning.

'It would, sir.' I choked on my words as I realised I was going home that day.

'We will send you a court date when it has been booked, approximately in two months' time. This will give you time to get your evidence and witnesses available for us. Young lady, this day is for you to say all you need to say, and I mean everything. Would you be prepared to accept another interview of your daughter by a court welfare officer?'

'Yes, sir', I said 'as long as I don't have to leave my house and it's not Mrs Statham.' He conferred with his two colleagues and I saw them all nodding in agreement. I started to feel I was finally getting somewhere. Billy's face had turned to thunder. He stared at me in a final attempt of intimidation. Only this time he was seen by all three magistrates on the bench. The gentleman turned again towards me.

'I suggest you leave this court and find anyone and any proof of his violence to help your case. If, however, you don't convince us at the next hearing and then don't comply with our decision, you will be given a custodial sentence for contempt of court; believe me young lady, you will go to prison.'

I thanked him and walked free from the courtroom.

'Well done Jeannette - get as much information as you can to fight your case. I will send you an appointment through the post to come and see me to see how you are getting on. Good luck and don't worry - you can do this,' said a pleased Mrs Radford.

'Do I have to let Lilly go in the meantime?'

'No, she stays with you now until the court's final decision. Try and stay out of his way - with that look on his face he knows you're determined to fight him and I think if we do this right, we will win.'

I thanked her for her help in the courtroom and she smiled - leaving to go to another client who needed her.

Exhausted with emotional stress, I sat quietly in the car on my return to mum's house. I decided to stay at mums for a while knowing Billy would be furious; if he thought he was going to be beaten over his daughter he wouldn't care what happened to him, as long as he had finished me off first. The threats he made when I was pregnant with Lilly, "you ever try and take her away from me I'll blow your fucking head off" resounded around my head. I had been fighting for over three years and taken all he and the courts could throw at me: 'staying strong' now was a must. So, having picked up Lilly from her hideaway, I decided for the meantime mum's was the safest place to be - with the dogs and a high wall surrounding us. Mum was quite happy to have us and loved the company - but knowing her family was safe was most important. As I thought about the day's proceedings, I was amazed where I had conjured up so much strength. Maybe it came out of fear or just sheer willpower, but what it did show me was I wasn't beaten yet - and with a few weeks to work on the next hearing I was sure I could end this fiasco once and for all. For the rest of the day I spent time with my girls and mum, thankful I had them.

The Letter

Ellen, my sister-in-law and old school friend, had followed with interest and concern what the continual trauma of courts appearances - intimidation and harassment - had been doing to my mental health. I once again felt imprisoned by fear and Billy's threatening behaviour. The day after the committal hearing Ellen visited me at mum's and suggested a way that might help to force the courts to re-evaluate Billy's capabilities of being a father to Lilly.

Intrigued and appreciative of any assistance - I welcomed her idea.

'We write a letter,' she suggested, 'and send it to every organisation in the country outlining what one man has done to you and your girls and how you're now being treated by the courts - their lack of support and professionalism in such a serious matter.'

This seemed a good idea, but I was wary of upsetting the courts; if they thought I was complaining they weren't doing their job right, it could go against me and they could ignore whatever I said and send me to prison for daring to be so insolent.

'No,' she continued, 'they wouldn't dare because not only will the organisations support you in such a dire matter, but we will send one to the city paper, they would love to make a story out of it - if you are sent down you would be out the same day. In fact the court would have no choice but to take you seriously, Jeannie.'

'Okay Ellen, let's do it.' I knew the fight had begun.

I contacted Natalie and asked her to come and see me: on the promise Billy would never find out, she agreed. She arrived two days later at my home - a little worried why I needed to see her. I made her feel very welcome and chatted about her children and asked how she was - making sure I kept Billy out of the conversation.

'How are you after the Court case last week?' She asked. I wasn't sure whether she genuinely cared or she was checking me out to report back to Billy. If I had learnt anything through this -it was not to trust anyone except family and my solicitor.

'Oh. It was just another court case. I should be used to them by now.' I nonchalantly commented. I made her tea and opened some biscuits - I knew she wouldn't have been eating much because she resembled the skeletal frame I remembered. Her eyes showed the darkness that recurring bruises caused. We sat chatting as she enjoyed the company of an understanding ally. I wanted her to discuss how their days were spent when Lilly used to visit, so carefully opening up the conversation, I smiled and said,

'Anyway, thank you for looking after Lilly every Sunday when she came to yours. I did worry about her until I knew she was with you and your kids.'

'Oh she is a pleasure to be with, our kids love her. It's just a shame he had to be there.'

Partially laughing I said, 'Who Billy?'

'Yes that waster of a space. I can't believe how he tormented the little mite - always digging at her and bossing her around.'

'Well that's dads for you,' I replied, making a mental note of all she was saying. 'What did me is the way he kept leaving her so he could go to the pub.'

'Well to be honest, Lilly was glad he went - she could relax and play better. She was happy with us. She would have her dinner and play all day 'til he came back and then he'd take her to his mam's.'

'What, at lunchtime?'

'No,' she laughed out loud. 'When did Billy ever leave the pub till they threw him out at closing?' She continued to think it funny and I joined in with her laughter.

'So he was drunk most of the time then?'

'Oh yeah, he hasn't changed from when he was with you.' Her face began to look subdued. 'You know, you were lucky to get rid of him.'

'I ran for my life, Natalie, and I never really have got rid of him. I live with his threats constantly and this is the reason I'm fighting to stop him using Lilly against me. He doesn't want Lilly - he just can't face losing the battle. He hates me.'

'He hates women full stop,' she retorted.

'I know - I worry about Lilly when she gets older - look what he did to Anna. He's a danger to kids but try proving it: he's too clever to get caught out.' I sat quietly for a moment watching her eat biscuits and drink her tea.

'To be honest, Jeannette, I hope you beat him. I know how he is with my girls.'

The more she spoke, the more ammunition I was receiving.

'He is so violent to kids he made Anna's life a misery - it was only to get to me after I became numb to his beatings. It broke my heart but I had to send her to Mark's for safety.' Natalie personally knew Mark - so I hoped she would open up a little more.

'He's okay I bet Mark was angry with what happened.'

'Of course, but as soon as I was away from Billy, he let me have her back.'

'That's good.'

I had to somehow get round to the court hearing in a few weeks' time - without frightening her off. I began talking about her children.

'Do your kids like Billy?'

'They're scared to death of him when he's been drinking. Sally left to go to her dad's many times - she caused so much trouble with Billy. Katie hides till he's gone to sleep.' Natalie partially laughed through embarrassment and shame. I knew how she was feeling. Though I felt sorry for her, Lilly's safety was paramount.

'You need to get away from him gal, as when you do he won't haunt you like he does me over Lilly.' I dropped my tone low using her sorrowful demeanour to lure her into my plan. 'The thing is, the courts don't believe he drinks when he's got Lilly and one of these drunken days he's going to beat her like he did Anna. I need some proof – somehow - someone to stand up in court and say he drinks on a Sunday.'

I left the living room and made a fresh pot of tea; when I returned she had gone outside to smoke a cigarette. I poured the tea and patiently waited for her return. Once again seated - she picked up her fresh cup of tea.

'What's it like in court?'

'It's just like talking to me, yes, it looks frightening but they are only people - people who want the truth - so they can make the right decision.' My heart was racing; hoping what I had planted into her head was working.

'And you only want someone to say - he drinks when he has Lilly?'

'That's all, but it seems the hardest thing in the world, someone I can trust to help me.' I took a sip of my tea, praying her help would be offered.

'I could say that for you, if, that's all I have to say. I won't tell them about the violence though - he might hit them to hurt me - for going against him'. She pondered a little while then asked 'when is it?'

'In about seven weeks - in the city.'

'I suppose I could catch a bus.'

'I could get you a lift if you want', I suggested calmly, not wanting her to think I was desperately in need of her. I didn't want to force her I knew, the consequences of going against Billy Burnshaw. It had to be her willingness to help that got her into court. I didn't want the repercussions on my hands - I had enough to worry about.

'Think about it, Natalie, and let me know, but it would help Lilly to be safe. I'm big enough to look after myself but that poor mite … anyway you make sure it's what you want to do. You know you can pop down for a cup of tea whenever you want. Just don't bring him with you.' I laughed, in an attempt to make everything seem light-hearted.

As Natalie got to the door, she turned.

'I'll help you Jeannette, someone's got to. I will ring you in a few weeks then you can tell me where and when. Bye for now.'

'If you ever need a safe haven, Natalie, come here with your kids.' Her smile thanked me a million times. I felt devious but I needed her in court and although she could back out - at least there was a chance of evidence now.

The following week Ellen arrived holding an envelope in her hand.

'I've done my best - but if you want anything changing - just say so. I'm not staying. I want you to read it and decide without pressure. Ring me when you're ready.'

I waited until I had peace and quiet after the girl's bedtime.

To whom this may concern:

I am writing to you as a desperate woman in need of some assistance.

I am facing a prison sentence for doing something any mother would do; protect my child of four-years. For over three years, I have been fighting court battles to ensure her safety. I am continually made to send her to a father, who time and again has proved to be unfit and violent. Having lived with this man for almost three years, I endured weekly violence and abuse, physical, mental and sexual.

In that time he beat my eight-year-old daughter so violently she went to her father's for safety; her father is willing to witness this fact, but the courts are not interested because it is my daughter Lilly they are concerned with. I have told of the horror of abuse to Lilly which included her being burnt with cigarettes, smacked and being dropped after an alcohol-fuelled-drinking session, resulting in shock and medical assistance. He continually drinks on access visits, even though a court order forbids it. I receive continual threats and intimidation and we live as prisoners in our own home. My daughter pleads with me not to send her, she is afraid of his tormenting, bullying nature. As her mother, I find this impossible to do and I am now fighting to stay out of prison for contempt of court. I have one more chance but I'm afraid I will be sent away leaving my children motherless.

Please is there anything you can do to help me and my children?

Yours sincerely

I sat absolutely stunned by what I had just read. There was nothing to be changed. Ellen understood the situation perfectly. I rang to thank her. After a brief conversation I used the telephone directory to find appropriate welfare organisations and the address of the city press. Taking a copy to Mrs Radford on my next visit to make sure I wasn't doing anything detrimental to my case. During the reading of the letter - I saw a slight smile on her face.

'Well done, Jeannette. I see you are ready to beat him at last. Yes, this should be fine to send. May I keep this copy? Is there anything else you have been able to come up with?'

'I have had a good chat with Natalie, Billy's partner. She told me she is willing to come to court to verify his drinking while he has Lilly and the fact he spends virtually no time with her.'

'That's excellent work, Jeannette. Now, how sure are you she will turn up at court?' I could see - though pleased with my headway - she doubted Natalie's appearance and deep down, so did I.

'I won't depend on her - it will just be a bonus. I will do my best to encourage her, but she is as scared of Billy as I was. He is repeating his behaviour and although I feel sorry for her - I have to put Lilly first.'

She nodded in agreement, but was still impressed with my determination to win.

Within the following week I received numerous replies from the organisations after receiving my letter, the NSPCC (National Society for the Prevention of Cruelty to Children) was a great support but because it was an on-going case - their hands were tied - until after the court's decision: if it was to go against me, they would certainly take a keen interest in the reasons why. The other replies were more or less the same but all wished me well and would be awaiting the outcome. The city newspaper, although saying virtually the same thing - gave me a telephone number - to call immediately in-case I was incarcerated - they would then lead the campaign to overturn the decision securing my release. One wet, dreary morning a knock rapped on my door; a bedraggled woman with an umbrella asked:

'Ms Preston?' Her smile and happy voice lifted my spirits.

'I am.'

'Oh it's lovely to meet you. I'm Sue from Family First - you wrote us a letter?'

I invited the poor drenched woman in and put the kettle on to make her a hot drink. She had caught the bus and made an eight-mile journey from their office to bring their support and discuss the problems.

'We can't actually do anything - we haven't any powers on the legal side of things. All I can offer is someone to talk to - at any time of the day or night. Your letter touched everyone in our office - we feel for you and your daughters deeply. If there is anything we can do, for example go with you to the courts to give you support or help you in your dark moments, please don't hesitate ring this number and someone will be there for you.'

She left around an hour later with a smile that lit up my day. There may have not been anything anyone could do - but the immense support from all who had read my correspondence gave me the confidence to do what had to be done: to stand up and bare my soul to the court. I knew the truth would be all I needed.

Eventually the telephone call from the court welfare officer came in order to make an appointment to visit. We arranged for the following Wednesday. I realised the court date had been arranged - soon - I would know our fate. He introduced himself as Mr Graham his attitude more relaxed than the Statham woman. I felt at ease with him and while I made him a welcomed drink - he set up some children's games on the dining table. Giving Lilly juice and placing her at the table I told her,

This is Mr Graham and he wants to talk to you.'

'Like that lady, mummy?'

'Yes, sweetie, but he's much nicer look, he's brought games for you to play. Now I'll be in there, (pointing to the living room), so if you need me I'm not far away.' Lilly nodded, as she looked into my eyes, I saw hers were full of trust. I hoped I had the guts to see this through. I smiled and turned to walk away, when I heard Mr Graham say in a quiet gentle voice,

'Don't worry, she will be fine.'

I left the two of them chatting and playing games. Closing

the door to allow her to keep her thoughts private - I sat and waited. I could hear laughter and talking but couldn't make out any of their words. It lasted an hour which seemed never-ending. Suddenly she burst through the doors in an excited state, running straight for her dolly - then returned to the dining room.

'Here she is,' her voice shrieking with happiness, 'she's my best dolly.' I smiled and waited until Mr Graham entered through the door.

'Thank you,' he said with a beaming smile.' I will make my recommendations to the court.' As he left, he commented on what a 'happy little girl' Lilly was.

Lilly didn't offer any information on the conversation or play with Mr Graham, so I allowed her - her privacy. We took a walk to the end of the street to meet Anna from school, then on to mum's house. The memories of 202 were too much for both Anna and I. All the houses around us became empty so the council offered me a bigger house in order to work on the six empty houses consecutively without inconveniencing tenants. This suited us fine: the girls now had their own rooms and we were just around the corner from mum, whose heath was deteriorating. I told mum the meeting seemed to go well this time, but we both knew with a devious, manipulating man like Billy nothing could be taken for granted.

Final Judgement

It had taken almost five years to get to this day. Five years of threats, violence, intimidation, tears and fear. Three of those years were spent in and out of a courtroom. This day gave me the worst feeling of all. I knew the outcome would impact on my life dramatically - whichever way the judgement went. I was unusually calm: my family knew I was stubborn and this could lose me my liberty. The only thing for sure was that Lilly would be safe, what-ever the courts decided. I looked forward to being imprisoned or forever looking over my shoulder. Surviving Billy's attacks proved I was strong enough to cope what-ever the eventual outcome. I had secured Lilly with a trusted friend for the day, a friend who Lilly adored. If I didn't return, I had made arrangements for my friend to keep her safe for as long as it took. Anna had been taken to her paternal grandmother's with instructions to return her to her father if I was incarcerated. Everything had been put into place. I promised both my daughters this man would never hurt them again. I intended keeping my promise. Everything hung on persuading the court - I wasn't a liar or a vindictive - spurned ex-partner intent on begrudging a loving father time with his child. In essence, I needed to show them they had made - an error of judgement.

After saying a painful and sad goodbye to my children, I returned home in preparation to face my future. I ran myself a bath and decided to put all negative thoughts out of my mind. I choose a smart black trouser suit and a crisp white blouse hoping they could see the difference between me and the slovenly, unkempt Billy. I tied my long blonde hair neatly away from my face - to enable the magistrate's to see - I wasn't hiding anything. Prayers filled my head constantly. I endeavoured to keep all nerves at bay. I asked God to give me the strength to do what I needed to do. For the first time everyone was going to hear the degrading, abusive torment this man had put me and my family through.

While waiting for my lift to appear, I looked around the home I had made for me and the girls. Their photographs on the mantle along with the ones of my parents gave me the strength to fight alone - once more. The enormity of what I was doing began to dawn on me - was I really strong enough to cope in prison? For a slight moment nausea took over. I fought to keep control as I fussed our faithful pet dog. I checked I had the newspaper's telephone number, it may be needed. I recounted a conversation with the barrister who represented me in the eyeball incident. I realised why he had said what he did.

'There is only one way to beat this man, and that is to move to the other end of the country, making access impossible.'

Was he right? Or would Billy have followed me?

I remembered asking,

'Why should I run away? I have done nothing wrong; I'll fight him if I have to.'

'To be safe.'

Maybe I should have taken his advice. Billy was violent and I thought the law was there to protect victims, not to allow him to continue his control and intimidation. Deep down I knew he wouldn't stop his campaign of hate - wherever I lived - until he had Lilly and I was either imprisoned or dead.

The car arrived, having picked up mum first. With a lump in my throat I took a deep breath saying out loud to myself,

'It's the day you've been waiting for Jeannie, so make it count. Be strong - you can beat this monster once and for all.'

With one last look around my lovely home, I locked the door behind me, giving my mother the door key.

'Here, mum, you may need this.' I forced a smile as she took it from my hand.

The journey to the city court was solemn. I didn't want to talk to anyone. I needed to concentrate on quashing any nerves or negativity that arose. The closer the city got, the more my heart quickened. I sensed mum was afraid for me, but she agreed on the stance I had to make. The possibility of going to prison scared the life out of me, but I knew what Billy was capable of and if I could survive that, I could survive prison. I was tougher than anyone thought, even I.

It had seemed impossible to beat the system: without evidence, even my solicitor knew I was going to struggle. I had evidence; I was the evidence, me and my story. Today the truth had to win through because that was all I was taking into the courtroom with me. I felt a little more confident with the precedents I had discovered in the law books at the local library, stating 'a child was not to be forced against its will - if there was suspicion of abuse'. It showed me courts can make mistakes and with a little respect and gentle persuasion - I was sure I could make them see this was one of those times.

It was going to be a closed court; no-one but those involved were going to be allowed in the room at any time, so I could speak freely. This went some way to ease my shame at the consequences of meeting a man like Billy Burnshaw. It wasn't going to be easy reliving the mental, physical and worst of all, sexual abuse to the court. My only witness was Natalie and I wasn't sure she would appear. In her position, I would be terrified to stand in a court of law against this man. It was a lot to ask of her and I understood and would forgive her if she had a change of heart. Mrs Radford said she could have been summoned on my behalf. I didn't want that, it would be her free will or nothing. I was once in her shoes.

I reached the top of the stairs where I headed for the courtroom - flanked by my two burly bodyguards. I arrived at the waiting area to find Billy in a suit and tie, sitting alone. I realised then he intended to see me locked up. I didn't look into his monstrous eyes. I needed to stay focused. I heard Mrs Radford call my name - obviously eager to keep me away from Billy and his intimidation. Her sincere smile blew away all doubts whirling around my head: knowing she had faith in me and had done through the three years she had fought by my side gave me the strength I clearly needed.

'Great, you're a little early. Come into this room, we need to have a quick chat,' she opened a door to my left. I followed her like a little lost sheep pretending to be a lion. As we sat Mrs Radford went over the court protocol with me.

'You may find it a little scary in there - it's going to be very intense. You have to tell them everything you remember about the violence to you - not just to your daughters. They have to build a picture in their minds to understand why you're adamant about banning access. They need to hear what a bully and violent man he is. You're going to have to bare your soul. It's very rare a court will revoke all rights of the father and that is what we are here to do.'

She looked pensive but sympathetic. I don't think deep down even she thought I had the nerve to do what she had asked, 'to bare my soul'.

I looked into her big brown eyes as she continued,

'No-one will be allowed in court except for the officials and, of course, Billy. You can say everything you need to without your family listening to you. You need to stay focused, honest and sincere in what you say. Don't waver in any way and try to keep your emotions under control. We have discussed what happened to you - now go and tell them. I know you can do it.' As we stood to exit the room she continued, 'I will lead you if I think you have forgotten anything, but this is your time, Jeannette - let's beat him.' Her smile showed her confidence in me and gave me the strength to walk into the courtroom and face the monster one more time.

I entered the empty courtroom, looking at the bench where the magistrates would sit in judgement. All fear and emotion left me; I became calm and self-assured. Knowing Lilly was in safe arms gave me the right frame of mind to fight only this time I wasn't going to end up physically bruised. I turned to the door when I heard it open – it was the two burly security guards who entered and stood at the back of the room in front of two chairs behind Mrs Radford's seat. From there they could see every movement Billy made. I felt safe, for now. I turned away from the door, knowing Billy would be entering any moment to take his seat: to do so, he had to pass behind me. I sat rigid waiting for the scuffle behind me. Mrs Radford turned to speak to acknowledge Billy's solicitor. My eyes were locked on the front of the courtroom. I couldn't afford anything to deter my mind from its focus. I felt Mrs Radford's hand touch mine, which steadied my inner nerves that were building. Turning towards her, my face feeling taut under the strain, I saw Billy out of the corner of my eye. I heard the side door open and a court usher entered from the right: he took his place at his desk.

'All rise.'

My nerves tried to take over as I began to feel alone in my battle. I fought to stay upright as my legs began to buckle beneath me. Three people entered through the door from which the usher had appeared; one gentleman and two ladies took their place at the highly polished bench. The man was seated on the left. I realised he was the one that saw something in me at the committal hearing and decided to give me the benefit of the doubt. My eyes moved steadily to the one on the right, an elderly lady. I remember thinking she looked like she hadn't had a frightening experience in her life. I looked intensely at the lady in the middle who was of large build and seemed much younger than her associates. Her dark hair fell into curls around her face: she looked a stern woman who would not take any nonsense. As they settled themselves into their roles as judges of my life, I turned to Mrs Radford, asking her if they were the same ladies from the last hearing.

'No only the man,' her voice low and confident.

The hope of standing a chance of winning, with fresh ears and eyes of the women - the man who had a slight interest into why I am being so stubborn - in my fight to stop Billy's access, was beginning to lift my spirits. The courtroom fell even quieter than it already seemed. I turned to look at Billy's solicitor, at the man who would try and prove me a liar and ruin my life even more than it already had been in my twenty-nine years. I recognised him immediately: I knew I had seen him before. I was shocked to see he was the man three years earlier - who had met me on the road near his office - then handed me my file. Surely that wasn't right? He had heard the case first hand, from me. I didn't know whether or not to tell Mrs Radford, I really needed to proceed today - I had prepared myself and I couldn't bear a postponement. I quickly decided to keep quiet in the hope that he didn't recognise me.

I felt the burning eyes of the magistrates bearing down on me as I lifted my head and looked in their direction, wondering when and how things would begin. The lady in the middle took a deep breath, her nostrils flaring and her eyes set on the warring parents before her, then she spoke.

'Before we start this case, I would like to remind you of the story of 'Solomon' in the Bible.'

After a moment's silence, she spoke again.

'Please, Mrs Radford, proceed.'

It had begun.

Mrs Radford explained why we were there that day. She asked them to take the time to seriously consider why I would risk a custodial sentence if I didn't truly think my daughter was in danger at the hands of Mr Burnshaw.

'My client will explain her fears under oath; she has done everything possible to facilitate the access of Lilly to her father. He has totally disregarded the initial court order three years ago, where my client's only fear was that Mr Burnshaw would and has taken Lilly to licensed premises. He has also left her for five of the seven hours of access during his appointed day each week with his parents or his girlfriend, while he has visited licensed premises to drink alcohol, when he was specifically ordered by the court - not to do so. My client will tell you of his temper and violence, especially when he has alcohol in his system and in the case of her daughter Anna - how he soberly beat her so violently, she was forced to leave the family home for her own safety. My client has strongly urged all child protection and welfare authorities of her fears pertaining to her child's safety via letter.'

'Yes, Mrs Radford,' the magistrate intervened, 'we have been privileged to see a copy of this letter.'

My mind raced as I tried to figure out how they could have obtained a copy of the letter in question.

Mrs Radford continued.

'I intend to show you that my client genuinely fears for her daughter's life, as she does for her own and that of her eldest daughter, Anna.'

'Please remain seated, Ms Preston.' She turned towards me. 'Can you tell their Honours in your own words - how your life has been while you were the partner of Mr Burnshaw and the continuation of threats since you escaped. Also, what are your fears for you and both your daughters and why?'

I took a calming deep breath; I looked straight at the three people at the end of the room, sitting high on their seat of judgement and began the fight for - my Lilly.

'When I met Billy ...'

I told how nice and charming he was in the first ten months of our relationship and how Lilly was happily planned. How, when I was four-and-a-half months' pregnant he changed and began the violent attacks - how the first beating was so severe - I was in shock for days - after his threat of ripping 'that baby out of my stomach' if I attempted to leave. The magistrate's faces drained as I continued to tell them it wasn't a regular occurrence at first, but a month later it happened again only more vicious than the time before - always happening after he had been drinking alcohol. Then I told of the ordeal of being tipped out of bed because Anna's father had rung in an attempt to bring her home early - due to him being ill. I recounted the name-calling and the fact I was trapped under the bed - being left to climb out from underneath, which was a struggle as I was six-and-a-half months' pregnant with Lilly. At this point, I knew by their faces I had their undivided attention.

'Then the rapes began.' I saw the older lady flinch as I recalled 'I was just over seven months' pregnant, but he didn't rape me like he would rape a woman.' I couldn't ever use the term that explained what he did, but this time was different. 'He sodomised me.' I spoke in a weak, ashamed voice. This also shocked Mrs Radford - I hadn't been able to bring myself to tell her I had suffered terrible sexual abuse other than rape. I continued to explain the sequence of events, not once turning my eyes from my judges. Their expressions turned to horror as I continued. 'This, too, became the norm when he thought the beatings weren't enough to demoralise me. I lived in fear of what he would do to me next. Derogatory name-calling was an everyday occurrence even in front of my daughter, Anna.'

I saw while I was recounting the catalogue of events, they would look at me in disbelief, their faces drawn into pale shades of grey as they listened to my horrific tale. I was no longer afraid of them or Billy. The words continued to flow as I continued telling how he threatened my parents with the hammer to terrorise me and the ensuing fight for the offending object, which amused him. I told them how I lived under the belief he was capable of doing everything he threatened. I explained how he would keep Lilly away from me, especially if she was crying for me. He was so jealous of the fact we were close, even though that's how it should be between mother and baby, he caused me to stop breast-feeding because he would degrade me calling me derogatory names like 'fat milking cow', which was a prelude to being beaten. I told how he wouldn't let me feed her fresh food and vegetables - he would only allow her eat sweet things; ice cream and sweets to encourage her away from me and solidify the bond between them. All it did was to ruin her teeth and make her hyper. He even refused to let me teach her manners 'please' and 'thank you' - in his opinion - she wasn't a dog to be trained. The look of disgust appeared across their faces, as I told them he wouldn't let the relationship between Lilly and her sister Anna, develop. Saying how they weren't allowed to play together, which caused hurt to both of them, and how Anna was afraid to interact with her baby sister even when Billy was out, because she thought I would get beaten if he found out I had allowed them to play. Anna was six years old. I told them how he paraded me around when I was black and blue through the beatings, as if he was telling the world he controlled me. I said how I truly believed my fate was death because he hated me because I was a woman.

'My daughter is female - how long will it be before she bears the bruises he can no longer give me?' I asked.

I continued to shock them with the stories of Lilly's cigarette-burns and his laughter the first time it happened and that he did it twice more. The dunking of Anna in a cold bath and the derogatory names he would call her in public because of her wetting the bed, which she had started through the fearful life she was experiencing in the home. I told of the incitement of a female friend of his to attack me on a night out, but having stood up to her she backed down, which made Billy so furious that he attacked me on the way home. I described the railing incident at the convent. Though the magistrates were impartial,

I could see by their expressions they had never heard such stories of sickening violence. The older lady again flinched as if she was putting herself in my position. I felt for the first time I was being believed. I couldn't stop talking: there was so much to tell them. Occasionally, their eyes left mine and looked at Billy. I too occasionally looked across at him, then quickly back to the three mesmerised magistrates.

The magistrates saw Billy's reaction to my words. He looked out of the window most of the time, taking no interest in what I was saying. I could see the sympathy appearing in my judge's faces as they listened to the catalogue of violence, the physical, sexual and mental intimidation we had all endured. No longer did they look sternly at me: the gentleman on the bench sat back in his chair as if he couldn't believe what he was hearing. I explained the reason I didn't go to the police or seek outside help was because I was so traumatised by what was happening to me and his threats to my daughters were, in my mind, real. He told me no-one would believe me, or if they did, I would be blamed for it, all of which seemed to be the case in previous court hearings. Billy drilled into me that no-one liked me, let alone loved me; he instilled into me I was useless and deserved my punishment. That's why nobody came to see me or help protect me from him. After all - I had killed my son (I explained that my second child, Anna's full brother, was stillborn and that Billy had drilled into me it was my fault). I told them how I took the responsibility for Anna's beating, because Billy said if I did then her father wouldn't report me. If I told them the truth, then Lilly would be put into care. In my weak and confused state, I had believed every word he told me.

I took a few minutes to collect myself: what I been telling the court was taking its toll and I needed a minute or so as I prepared myself to recount another painful ordeal. I sipped water from the glass in front of me and cleared my throat. After taking a deep breath, I resumed my catalogue of terror.

'I had put the girls to bed, even though he had ordered me not to. They were tired and it was late around 10pm. I wasn't allowed to go to bed myself it would instantly result in being woken up, either being physically or sexually attacked. I had come to the conclusion it was easier to be punished away from the children because the ferocity of some of his attacks was so evil - the girls witnessing the abuse - was just another worry, adding stress to my already panicked state. I had sat in a chair watching the road for Billy's drunken return. It was about 10.40pm and I'd felt my body start to tremble. I knew I had done wrong in putting the girls to bed and would suffer the consequences. I had held onto my legs in order to stop the trembling, but by then my whole body began to shake uncontrollably. I was petrified - there was nothing I could do because the fear of Billy's imminent arrival had put my body into total terror. Suddenly, I started to make noises from my mouth, squeaks and high-pitched cries. I was unable to stem the sounds of my fear. Still watching for Billy to come down the hill opposite the house, the noises increased.

I wasn't able to move, my legs wouldn't hold me up. I heard the clattering of metal as the latch on the gate grabbed the catch. I wet myself in fear. When he'd seen the state of me he laughed. He taunted and mimicked me as I shook and winced in terror before him. He kneeled directly before me with an inane grin on his face. He'd begun to tell me what he was going to do to punish me for ignoring his order of keeping the girls up. True to his word, with one hand around my throat, my frail skeletal body was hoisted out of the chair - by then I was almost 3-stone underweight - at that point he realised the chair was wet and so was I. I cannot tell you what expletives he'd yelled: his voice was a blur. I'd tried to shut off from the pain as he'd slammed my face into the floor and dragged me across the carpet, burning the right-hand side of my face. He punched and kicked me until I'd been barely conscious. I'm sure he had gone to bed that night leaving me for dead. It was the early hours when I'd regained consciousness; I remember being wet and covered in blood. Too afraid to go upstairs for clean clothes I'd found some dirty clothes in the washing machine.'

I lowered my head. The quietness of the courtroom was echoing.

'I have lived in his fear for over five years: even in this environment where I am supposed to feel safe, especially with bodyguards at the back of me, I am wary of being attacked. I know what he is capable of. I have lived in terror at his hands. I know I will never be safe in this world while he lives, but I can make sure he doesn't hurt my children - ever again.'

I told them how desperate I was to protect my family, hence the request for help from the NSPCC and the child welfare agencies. I feel I am not being listened to. I said I appreciated they must see many cases of this nature, but that I wasn't vindictive and Anna had a good relationship with her father and he didn't hesitate to return her - on the understanding I didn't go back to Billy.

It was like someone or something was there by my side, helping me to remember the sickening hurt and abuse we had all suffered. I heard the words 'Stay Strong' quietly spoken. After reliving my torment, my emotions were raw. I had indeed 'bared my soul'. I finished by saying,

'If I mother my child for six days a week, keeping her safe, clean and loved, then you take her away from me for the seventh day - sending her to a man she fears and begs me not to send her - because he hurts her, then I'm sorry. I can't mother her at all, what woman could?'

Billy stopped looking out of the window as he realised what I had done.

I had turned his words back on him. I'd taken a chance. When Billy was causing trouble with Anna's access to Mark a few years earlier, he'd said I had to stand in the court hearing and say that I couldn't mother her six days a week if she was to go to him for the seventh. I'd never said the words. Mark was a good daddy to Anna. Though I had told Billy I had said the words the court had taken no notice - so he wouldn't beat me. Today his words came back to haunt him.

Billy scowled, he knew I wasn't that scared, fragile woman he tried to send crazy. I remained calm as I returned his glare. I saw his eyes were turning green. I slowly returned my eyes to the magistrates. The three of them watched as I lowered my face at the shame of the degrading violent acts - I had just released from my mind. It was the first time I had told anyone the full extent of the abuse I had endured - at his hands. There were things even Mrs Radford hadn't heard. The courtroom was silent, so was I.

I had nothing more to say. I leaned back in my chair, my head still bowed. Mrs Radford patted my hand, which was riveted to the table before me.

In my silence I realised - the shame wasn't mine to carry - it was Billy's.

'You did well,' whispered Mrs Radford, a knowing smile comforted me. I had fought with all I had in my heart and I could do no more (except to give up my freedom). The stunned silence in the courtroom lasted for a few minutes, as everyone came to terms with what they had just heard.

Billy's solicitor's slight cough, to clear his throat before his cross-examination, broke the silence. I turned to face his questions. He was the man who three years ago hadn't got the guts to help me; now he was acting against me. I wasn't about to cower for him and sat straight-backed and returned his gaze. I could see Billy staring out of the window ignoring the proceedings. His solicitor dithered in his approach and seemed lost for words after the horrifying story he had just witnessed. Sitting for a few minutes he looked into my eyes. I could see even he believed me, but he had a job to do and that was to prove - I was a liar.

'I put it to you, Ms Preston, that none of this happened and that you are lying,' he spluttered, unsure he wanted to insult my intelligence.

I replied calmly but firmly.

'Then I should be a Hollywood scriptwriter to be able to make all this up.'

Again, the silence in the room was echoing. There were no more questions he could or wanted to put to me. He looked out of his depth, not knowing how to continue. He knew I was being truthful and so did the magistrates. The magistrates spoke between themselves, after which they lifted their eyes into the direction of Billy, who was still oblivious to the seriousness of the hearing. The gentleman on the bench asked if he had anything to add on his own behalf.

Billy exhaled loudly and shrugged his shoulders before growling,

'She's a liar,' he returned to his window-gazing.

I watched as the magistrates stared at him in disbelief. One by one they looked at each other, but didn't look in my direction. I daren't get my hopes up, not yet. I sat quiet and with dignity.

Mrs Radford's questioning of Billy was as short.

'Mr Burnshaw.' She waited a few minutes until he looked at her - this showed his ignorance and made my case stronger. 'Why do you think my client has made up all these stories if she is in your words - lying?'

Everyone's focused on him, intrigued to how he would reply. All they saw was Billy slumped in his chair looking bored, refusing to defend his actions or my words. I was pleased his manner was disrespectful - it showed him to be the person I had portrayed. He once again shrugged his shoulders and grunted words no-one could make out or even cared about.

'With that,' said the magistrate with the dark hair and with a more gentle voice by now, 'we will break for lunch.'

'All rise.' The three of them filed out with their heads bowed as if in thought.

'Is it that time already?'

'You have talked for two and a half hours nonstop, Jeannette, well done,' Mrs Radford quietly conveyed. 'You had better go and see if Natalie has turned up - we could do with her to back up your story.'

I left the courtroom with the two burly bodyguards immediately behind me. I saw mum's fraught face as she waited in anticipation. She immediately stood up - her face was ashen. Putting her arms around me she held me, but I think she needed the hug more than I did.

'I'm proud of you Jeannie, you're so strong. How did it go? You look exhausted.'

'Well it isn't over yet. Has Natalie arrived do you know? We need her.'

'No.' It was the answer I was dreading. I ran to the payphone in the foyer, the two security men followed in hot pursuit. I rang her telephone number hoping she would answer.

'Natalie,' I said, 'I need you. Don't worry you will be safe. I have bodyguards and they won't let him get to you. All I want you to do is tell them you fetch her and look after her on a Sunday that's all. It's important, please, Natalie. I can come now and fetch you and we will take you home immediately after, please,' I begged.

'Okay, if you promise to drop me off at my door after.' Her words were like music to my ears.

'On my way but you must be ready, we only have an hour.'

'I'm ready.'

I returned to the waiting room. I explained to the bodyguards, who had heard my conversation, that I had to fetch my witness or she wouldn't come. With their reassurance they would be at the door awaiting my return. I grabbed the arm of the car driver, leaving mum to explain to Mrs Radford where I had gone and promising we would be back in time. Within minutes we had left to fetch Natalie.

'I had every intention of coming to court, but I have no money for bus fare - he took it all', Natalie explained as I entered her house. I felt the presence of Billy even though I knew he was miles away in the city. I saw holes punched into walls and doors. The atmosphere was sad and dark smelling of stale alcohol and cigarettes. I reflected on the similarity to 202 on its repossession. I felt for her, but this was no time for emotions - we had thirty minutes to get back to the court. We were dropped off at the court building and were immediately greeted by the security men. We made our way to the waiting area, asking Natalie to wait while I checked Billy wasn't around the area. He wasn't. She closely followed behind me and sat down with mum.

'I have Natalie with me, she's with my mum,' I said, on finding Mrs Radford.

'I'm not saying that he hits anyone, he will kill me if I do,' Natalie said quickly in fear as she met Mrs Radford.

My solicitor looked at me as if to verify her trust in what I had been fighting for during the last three years. Turning back to Natalie she said,

'Please, don't worry,' calming her down. 'You will just be asked if you fetch her on a Sunday and how long she spends with you and your daughters.'

'That's okay then I can do that. Is he in the courtroom?' Natalie asked, looking nervously around her.

Mrs Radford could see she was terrified. Concerned for her safety, she asked her to wait in a room until Billy had been summoned back into court, on which she could return to the waiting area. I put my arm in hers and promised she would be safe as we escorted her into the room. Mum followed us in order to stay with Natalie while Mrs Radford and I headed for the courtroom for the afternoon continuation. Flanked by the burly bodyguards - who now knew the reason they were needed - I took my seat. Billy passed behind us stinking of alcohol; he had obviously spent the lunch hour in the pub across the road the aroma filled the air causing Mrs Radford to turn to me with a knowing smile. Soon the court was again in session.

'Your Honours,' began Mrs Radford, 'I would like you to allow the only witness that I will be calling today on behalf of my client: Natalie Dayton. She is at present the girlfriend of Mr Burnshaw.'

Billy turned to look at Mrs Radford in an attempt to intimidate her, the glare in his eyes changed as the monster in him began to rise. I hoped he would show the court his true self. He knew he was about to be proved the liar he was. My gaze remained on the faces of the magistrates. I could see their intense scrutiny of Billy as the courtroom door opened: they watched his reaction as Natalie was directed by the court usher into the witness box. I turned to see Natalie nervously clutching the frame of the witness box, looking terrified. I recognised fear in her eyes. She looked at me with a helpless expression. I smiled and nodded to her, she knew I needed her. I knew Mrs Radford would go to town on her until she got the evidence we needed. The feeling of guilt started to plague me. I felt sorry for her. I knew life would be hell for her when she got home and Billy found her later that day. I felt cruel but I needed to fight for my baby - by any means I had, and I hadn't forced her to do this. I kept my eyes away from Billy, keeping them firmly fixed on the table in front of me. I listened to the questioning of Natalie begin.

'Mrs Dayton - thank you for coming here today.' Mrs Radford's voice was friendly and gently reassuring. 'I understand that you are very nervous for various reasons but I have only a few questions for you today. Please remember you are under oath. Now, you are the present girlfriend of Mr Burnshaw, are you not?'

'I am,' Natalie's voice was squeaky with nerves as she replied. Clearing her throat, she forcibly repeated, 'I am.'

'And how long have you been with Mr Burnshaw?'

'Around three years, maybe a little under three.'

'And you know the child in question, Lilly?'

'I do'.'

'Could you explain to their Honours who is it who collects Lilly - on a Sunday morning from the home of my client?'

'It used to be Billy, then I did until she stopped coming. Billy was usually still in bed after his night out on a Saturday. I sometimes went in a taxi because it's a long way for Lilly to walk up to my house as she's only little.'

'Very thoughtful, Mrs Dayton,' remarked Mrs Radford in a caring manner. 'Is Mr Burnshaw up out of his bed when you return with his daughter?'

'Not usually, but he knows she's there - playing with my children.'

'Then when he gets up, what happens?' I daren't look at anyone. I listened intently to the questioning, wondering when Billy would explode.

'He gets up around half past eleven, gets dressed and washed, then goes to the club to have a drink and play cards.'

'Is that every Sunday?'

'Yes. If he hasn't the money - he takes it off me.'

'And where is Lilly when he leaves for the pub, sorry, club?'

'Playing with my kid's at my house.'

'So he doesn't really spend time with Lilly in the morning?'

'Not really he doesn't have time. He says hello, but she's too busy playing with my daughter; she loves my Katie.'

'And what time does Mr Burnshaw return home?'

'He doesn't. He goes to his mam's house for his dinner, so I take Lilly to him about 4.30pm. She even has her dinner at mine and then another at her grandma's when her dad gets home. I know he gets mad with Lilly sometimes because she won't eat it, because she's eaten with us. Well, I can't not feed her, can I, when we eat?'

'Of course not,' Mrs Radford agreed. 'So in the seven hours he is allotted for his access time, Lilly spends around what - five to six of them with you?'

'Usually yes,' Natalie replied.

'As Mr Burnshaw or you ever taken Lilly onto licensed premises during the hours of access?'

'We sometimes go to the pub up the road if he doesn't go to the club, but we sometimes go there too.'

'And during these times you're there with him at the club, does he play cards with his friends or does he play with Lilly?'

'Oh he likes to play cards. Lilly stays with me.'

'Do you know what Mr Burnshaw drinks, is it soft drinks like coke or is it alcohol?'

I heard Natalie partially laugh as she answered.

'Oh, he loves his beer.'

We did it: she said exactly what we needed her to say. I silently exhaled the deep breath I had nervously been holding inside. Mrs Radford asked her to stay where she was, as Billy's solicitor would like to ask her a few questions. I looked up from the table to nonchalantly glance at the magistrates. Their faces had a serious expression and they glanced back and forth between Billy and Natalie. I could see the disgust of the brunette. The emotion of the little old lady was being hidden as her lips tightened and her eyes continually blinked. The gentleman was watching me. I could see his sympathetic smile as he realised I had been telling the truth all along and had been fighting with all I had for both my daughters' wellbeing.

'Now then, Mrs Dayton,' began Billy's solicitor, sounding like he wished he wasn't involved in this case. 'Do you drink alcohol?' His voice was hesitant and slightly weak.

'Yes,' Natalie strongly replied as her confidence grew.

'When you have Lilly, do you drink?'

'Yes. But I'm not responsible for Lilly - he is,' she gestured towards Billy by the nod of her head.

'Not legally no, but she is left with you to be looked after, is she not?'

'Only, because he can't be bothered to keep out of the pub.' Natalie's voice was agitated at his implication she was to blame for anything.

Billy turned his head in Natalie's direction and, without being asked, stated,

'She's a bloody alcoholic - she hides bottles all over the house.'

'Be quiet, Mr Burnshaw. You will have your turn in due course,' said the brunette on the bench.

Billy expelled a loud deep breath in disapproval at her order: he shook his head, shrugged his shoulders and looked out of the window in annoyance.

'Are you an alcoholic, Mrs Dayton?' continued Billy's solicitor.

'Only because he drives me to it; my eldest daughter has been made a ward of court because of him and his violence,' her voice reaching a high pitch of anger.

I couldn't believe what she was saying and it was Billy that had caused her outburst. Billy's solicitor tried to quell her outburst, but found he had opened the proverbial can of worms.

'Please let her continue,' said the brunette magistrate.

Natalie turned to the brunette magistrate and continued to forcefully speak her mind.

'He hit my daughter, Sally, so her father went to the police. He told me I had to kick Billy out - but he wouldn't go - so her father took me to court and because of the violence Billy had used on her she was made her a ward of court, miss.'

I closed my eyes in disbelief at what I was hearing, but I silently thanked Natalie at the same time.

'How old are your daughters, Mrs Dayton?' asked the brunette magistrate.

'Sally is fourteen, Zoe is seven and Katie is five.'

'Thank you,' the magistrate made notes in her paperwork.

'No more questions, your Honour,' Billy's solicitor closed his file looking utterly lost for words. He knew he was completely out of his depth.

Natalie was thanked by the magistrates for attending on my behalf and was told she was free to leave the court.

'Can I go home?' Natalie asked, relieved her questioning was over.

'You may,' was the magistrate's reply, with a smile portraying her thanks. 'Mrs Radford - I take it you would like to ask Mr

Burnshaw a few questions?'

'I certainly do, your Honour.'

I could sense Mrs Radford's confidence and slight enjoyment as she began her questioning of the ignorant man seated at the far end of the table. I remained still, continuing to stare at the grey carpet beyond the table on the floor. I listened intently, but a little nervously at his response.

'Mr Burnshaw, could you tell me, why do you want to see your child Lilly?'

'Because she's mine,'

'Is it true you have two other children?'

'One yes, the other - well she went with some blokes at a party, I was accused of being the father.'

'Do you see any of them?'

'No.'

'Why is that, Mr Burnshaw?'

Billy shrugged his shoulders with no forthcoming answer.

'Do you pay child support for either of your children, including Lilly?'

'No, because I don't work' His voice was sarcastic and matter of fact.

'But weren't you working when you met Lilly's mother?'

'Not officially.'

Billy was making himself look completely and utterly stupid.

'Weren't you ordered to pay child support to the supposed daughter? I don't mean Lilly.'

'Yes, 50 pence a week.'

'Do you still pay it?'

'No.'

'Oh, even though there is a court order for you to do so Mr Burnshaw?'

Again he shrugged his shoulders giving no reply; he continued his gaze towards the window and ignored all other questions. His disregard for the law was obvious and his manner showed off his attitude towards his supposed children. Next to go into the witness box was the court welfare officer who had replaced Mrs Statham (I had learnt that she had been required to retire). I heard the door behind me open as Mr Graham entered the room. This time I was going to hear his report on my child. He stood in the witness box and was sworn in. Looking at him, I noticed the serious look on his face as he addressed the bench. I moved my hands from the table and placed them underneath, resting them on my knees, crossing my fingers on both hands. I kept repeating the word 'Please' under my breath. He explained who he was and his position with the welfare office. I saw the magistrates sort their paperwork and take out their copies of the report to refer to. I said he was the senior inspector and due to the immediate urgency of the case, he had decided to take the case himself after the previous officer dealing with it had unexpectedly retired.

He told the court how he had visited me and I had freely complied with his request to interview Lilly privately. He found Lilly to be a well-balanced, happy child. She was clear in her feeling towards both her parents and openly told of the fear she felt in being with her father and his family, although she loved her paternal grandmother, Billy's mother. He then visited Billy, but was greeted with the hostility of a man smelling of alcohol and cigarettes, who insisted that his family were present to make their feelings heard. When he came to tell the magistrates of his opinions on the case, he said,

'I feel there will be no detriment to Lilly if she never saw or had anything to do with her father again. She is happy with her mother and sister, though I feel there is still a lot of rebuilding to do after the past few years. She has a good support network with her mother, grandparents and extended family. I believe it is in Lilly's best interests to stay where she is with her loving, caring family.'

I felt my emotions warming inside, finally someone saw the real me and had listened to Lilly. I inhaled quietly, realising I hadn't won yet. He was thanked and released from court. It was short but straight to the point, and after Natalie's evidence I was sure we would win, but magistrates have their own opinions and I couldn't take anything for granted. After all, it was very rare they took a child completely away from its father and only a serious case would cause them to do so.

In summing up Mrs Radford said,

'Your Honours, I have been working on the tribulations of this case for three years and in all that time, my faith in my client has never wavered. What she has been through at the hands of this man you cannot imagine. She spoke of the life she endured, the violence, mentally and physically not only to herself but also to her children. There is no physical evidence, due to the fear and control he instilled into her. You have been told of the trauma caused to Anna through his violence, but who is now back living with her mother. She has recovered from her ordeal and is happy at home having a relationship with her sibling after Mr Burnshaw kept her away from her baby sister when she was a child of six years of age. There may not be proof of the violent attack being caused by Mr Burnshaw, but you have heard how Mrs Dayton's eldest daughter has since been made a ward of court due to his violence towards her: surely that is proof enough that my client is not lying. The word of his current girlfriend must be taken into consideration. My client has been prepared to hide Lilly from this man and risk a prison sentence, when her daughter Anna enjoys regular contact - even overnight stays - with her father. Does this show a vengeful woman or vindictive ex-partner? We hear how Lilly has now settled in school and doing well - her fear of her father is something that must also be taken into consideration. My client has endlessly campaigned to protect Lilly against all odds: she is terrified of this man, but the terror of her daughter being beaten and cruelly treated terrorises her more. So much so, she is prepared to accept a custodial sentence in order to make sure Lilly is taken into hiding for her own safety. Surely after hearing and watching the two of them in this courtroom, you must come to the right decision. Thank you.'

Mrs Radford sat down and closed her case file. That was it: we had done all we could.

'Do you wish to summarise?' Billy's solicitor was asked.

'There is nothing more I can say - your Honour - no - thank you.'

You could hear the disgust for his client in his voice. It was a silent and solemn courtroom. I knew he believed his client was the monster I portrayed - he possibly regretted believing a word he said. I sat tensed, listening to the muffled voices of the magistrates conferring between themselves, and then the brunette spoke.

'Thank you everyone for the information given to help our decision over Lilly. She paused. 'Before we retire to make our decision, I would like to remind you of the reading from the Bible I mentioned at the start of this case, 'The Story of Solomon'. Please think about this while you wait for our decision which, I might add, will be the last decision made in respect of Lilly and failure to comply will end in a custodial sentence.'

At that point I started to worry. They looked in my direction - her words hit to my core. I began to feel sick with nerves.

'All rise.'

I watched the magistrates as they left the room, filing out one by one through the side entrance.

'I know my Bible but I can't think - what do they mean by the story of Solomon?' Mrs Radford sensed the panic in my voice.

'The true lover of the child handed it over for a better life, rather than cut it in half,' she answered quietly, looking deeply into my frightened eyes.

Her sympathetic smile did nothing to appease me. She suggested I leave the room for a while to be with my mother and to take a break. This made me believe she was worried I would go to prison for contempt of court if the decision went against me. I walked through the door into the corridor where mum was sitting patiently. Our driver, sat with Natalie, who asked if it was over, could she could be taken home.

'Yes, we have done all we could. Thanks for what you said Natalie, I will never forget it. Get away from him for your kids' sake and your own.'

We hugged then she and our driver left for the drive back to her home. Mum and I sat quiet, hand in hand. I had done enough talking, my head hurt. We were both worried about my future and Lilly's life if I was to be imprisoned, but I knew I had to make a stand against violence in domestic circumstances.

The courts had to realise that error of judgement in these cases are easily made, due to the magistrates not having the time to listen to all the facts and that a cunning, devious, calculating abuser can control the situation to its advantage. It had taken three years for them to listen to me. After all it was only my stubbornness that got me my day in court. Not everyone is as strong as I - and the continuation of abuse and control makes a lot of lives - unbearable.

I had some hope: the local newspaper was awaiting the outcome and they would campaign to beat the legal system if I was imprisoned - my family would make sure of that. If I won, my children would finally be free of him, even though I would be looking over my shoulder for the rest of my life, knowing he was biding his time to wipe me out. Knowing Lilly wouldn't be made to go to our abuser and Anna wouldn't fear him coming to the door - made all this worth it. If I lost I wouldn't be there for either of them - they could grow up without me. I wouldn't give in to send Lilly to be hurt. I was prepared to stand by every word I had said. I knew in time my girls would understand my reasons and why I had to leave them.

The driver returned an hour later to see us still in the corridor. He joined us saying,

'Natalie is home safe, but she's terrified.'

'I know the feeling. She will sort something out to keep her and her kids safe, she's not stupid, she knows what he's like.'

We remained silent until I was called back in the courtroom. The court usher asked me to take my seat next to Mrs Radford. I felt the glare of Billy who had been told to stay inside the courtroom. I couldn't look at him, the security men were still seated and the atmosphere was gloomy. I took my seat and my solicitor smiled contently.

'Stay strong' I heard in my head. I wasn't sure who said it, my solicitor or my loving grandma. I had felt her presence around me when I was relating my life with Billy. I couldn't think of a single thing I had forgotten to tell them; it was as if it was being put into my head and I spoke what I heard. Maybe grandma was there in spirit and that's what she meant by the graveside when she told me to 'stay strong'. The side door opened and in came the three people who could free me from the torment of this man, or condemn me for protecting my child.

I started to shake with the pressure of the situation. I felt a hand on mine.

'Stay strong, it will be okay,' whispered Mrs Radford.

I took another deep breath and looked up. The brunette magistrate cleared her throat and started to address us.

'We have considered everything very carefully in this difficult case. I assure you the decision wasn't an easy one to reach. I reminded you before we retired of the story of Solomon. Mr Burnshaw,' she turned to look at him.

I could feel my legs trembling. I couldn't take my eyes off her mouth, anticipating her words. My mind was praying to God for help, begging him to free my Lilly from this man. I looked to the other magistrates for any indication of their impending judgement. There were no signs emanating from their hardened faces. I felt faint as fear gripped me; my mouth was dry. I stifled the cough my throat was trying to expel. Mrs Radford poured a glass of water and placed it in front of me, obviously hearing my struggle to control my fear. I stared at the cold refreshing water, but I dared not drink in case it choked me. I returned my eyes to the brunette woman, her face stern and serious, she began speaking to Billy.

'Mr Burnshaw, we have no doubt you love your daughter,' again pausing to take in a long drawn-out breath. I closed my eyes, straining my ears awaiting the verdict. She continued, 'but we feel you should give Lilly up for a better life. Access denied.'

I couldn't take in what she had said. I sat waiting for her to speak to me.

'All rise,' I heard for the last time.

I opened my eyes and stood as ordered, wondering what had happened. I saw the two female magistrates heading for the door, followed by the gentleman. As he drew level, he looked in my direction. He gave me a small apologetic smile as he followed the two ladies out of the courtroom. I saw in his eyes he was sorry that I had been put through the hell of this hearing. I bore him no malice.

'You did it - it was a worry, Jeannette, but you did it.' My solicitor congratulated me.

'Me?' I said with tears in my eyes, as the words 'access denied' sank into my stressed mind.

242

'I want you to sit there for a while until he is out of the building: my security will escort us out of the building when they are happy he has left. You just relax now and sit there to take in the fact that you have beaten him.'

Stunned, I fell to the chair. I saw Billy heading in my direction. I felt a terror run through me as he grew near; Mrs Radford remained standing and slightly covered his view of me. One of the security men stood at her side as the other one escorted Billy past me. I felt the slight gush of air as my abuser hurriedly strode by me; the smell of his cheap aftershave mixed with alcohol odour caused me to shiver from cruel and nasty memories.

'Just be aware how angry he will be. Can you stay at your mother's until he calms down, especially for the next few nights?'

'Yes,' nodding continuously, 'I will stay at mums.'

'Good,' she replied with a smile. Seeing the news was finally sinking in, she saw a smile take over my face for the first time in three years. I felt mum would be wondering what had happened, having seen Billy leave and no sign of. I didn't want her thinking I had been sent to the cells. I asked to go to her. Mrs Radford agreed, but warned me not to leave the building until she said it was safe.

I walked out of the door; the concern on mum's face turned to relief as she saw my smile. I burst into tears, relieved it was finally all over.

'We won mum, he can't have anything to do with her, ever,' I said, still taking in that I'd beaten him.

Mum stood up and rushed towards me; tears of joy were running down both our faces.

'Well done, oh well done.' Mum's voice was breaking as tears of pride began to flow.

'We can't go until security say we can, it's for my protection.'

I saw one of the suited, black-tied, huge men return to the corridor and go back into the courtroom. He returned a few minutes later with Mrs Radford.

'Ready?' She asked, smiling. 'She did excellent,' Mrs Radford said to mum as she patted my shoulder and repeated 'well done.'

'We certainly are,' I replied, drying the tears with my hands.

The big burly security man led the way down the stairs to the main door. We cautiously followed him. I saw the second guard standing outside of the main entrance door, making sure that Billy didn't return in vengeance. They both nodded to each other: as he exited the building he turned to me and nodded, adding a smile. They had been at my side for three years and had heard the degradation I had endured, but I saw respect in that smile. I smiled in gratitude for their protection. A returned smile showed me it was acknowledged. Mrs Radford led me out of the door, followed by my mum and the driver. We walked down the steps into the street where Mrs Radford dismissed security.

'I can never thank you enough, Mrs Radford,' I humbly said.

'My names Rebecca,' she replied, giving me her warm smile.

'Rebecca, thank you for believing in me,' I was a little choked.

'You're welcome, stay safe, and please don't take this the wrong way - I hope I never see you again.' A big smile took over her usually stern business expression.

'You won't,' I said, shaking her hand.

I turned away from her, taking in the sweet smell of freedom while heading off to collect: *my Lilly*.

January 2012

Lilly remained steadfast over the years and lives a happy contented life without Billy's intervention. She rebuffed any attempts by him to contact her once she became an adult. She has a loving, caring husband and up to now, two beautiful children. She is a vibrant, hardworking individual whose love for her mother and family is openly displayed.

Anna, although having the mental scars of her ordeal, has grown up to be an independent woman, with a loving partner and five beautiful children. She finds it hard at times to accept and show love to those who love her. The love inside her is enormous.

Natalie returned from court and fearing Billy's wrath, threw out his belongings, locked up her house and moved to the safety of her family - before Billy had a chance to find her. We remain friends.

Though my fear of Billy eventually eased, I was and never will be stupid enough to turn my back to him. Thirteen years after the court case, he reminded me of the last threat he made and warned me to be 'very careful'. After a talking-to from my brothers, the threats and intimidation stopped. I avoid Billy at all times.

My only regret is not having been brave enough to leave the first time Billy beat me.

Author's Note

It has been over twenty three years since Jeannette left the court with sole custody of Lilly. As with many cases of such violence, the perpetrator continued his campaign of control. Although her life has been spent looking over her shoulder - Jeannette never made the headlines or the national news, because she wasn't killed. Almost every week there is an incident of murder or maiming of victims - long after they have left their abusive relationship. This is why I felt compelled to bring the serious nature of Jeannette's story to your attention.

Jeannette's story conveys what can happen to your loved one, your daughter, your sister, or your friend - can all be hidden victims of heinous control and violence. It is a widespread issue that carries stigma and shame for the abused when in actual fact the shame belongs to the abuser.

If Jeannette's story can persuade one person, man or woman to listen to 'rumour' 'gossip' or 'tittle tattle' then the heart-breaking recount of her ordeal makes the arduous hours of writing such a cruel story worth every minute.

She has spent most of her adult life living alone - knowing she couldn't trust anyone if she couldn't trust herself to make the right choices. The feeling of being unlovable as scarred her deep within.

Jeannette's dream is a simple one. To eventually feel safe in this world.

A Little Friendly Advice

Domestic violence victims become very clever at disguising their life of abuse. Noticing changes in a usually happy - outgoing personality into - a sullen, withdrawn, despondent character - whose continual absence from family/friend gatherings - may be cause for concern - male or female. Men, also suffer behind closed doors at the hands of their wife/partner, may find it even harder to face the problem. Patience, friendship and an open door will serve to encourage them - to take the first step - to freedom.

If you suspect a friend or family member is acting in a nervous, subdued manner a helpline number discretely offered or slipped to them - may just change their life.

Remember: a victim of Domestic Abuse hides behind a wall of shame, silence and fear.

Organisations: *these are free and confidential.*

Freephone 24 hour **National Domestic Violence Helpline**. 0808 2000 247. Run in partnership between Refuge and Womens Aid.
DV Men: 'making sense of domestic violence on men.'**www. dvmen.co.uk** An informative online site for help and support.
The Freedom Programme: www.freedomprogramme. co.uk
Living with a dominator. A home study course - available in various language's for £10.00. Available at Amazon.com.

Learn to distinguish the signs in a person - who may be likely to abuse.